Silver *in the* Mine

A LONG TERM COMPREHENSIVE ENERGY PLAN FOR THE CITY OF AUSTIN

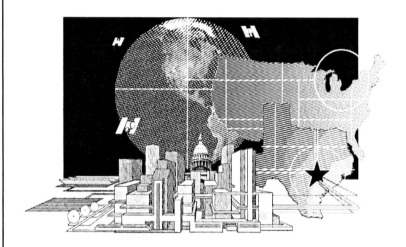

Austin Energy Publishing

Copies of Silver in the Mine are available through Austin Energy, 721 Barton Springs Road, Austin, Texas 78704 and local bookstores.

ISBN: 0-9679069-2-X
Library of Congress Number: 2003113350

Acknowledgments

This Community of the Future Initiative is the result of a joint agreement between the Department of Energy through its regional office in Denver, the State of Texas Energy Conservation Office, and the City of Austin.

I want to thank Doug Seiter, Glenn Jennings, and Ester Matthews for their efforts in making this partnership work effectively and efficiently.

I want to thank Roger Duncan for his leadership and vision.

I want to thank Juan Garza and the other Executives and Employees at Austin Energy for their help and good will.

There have been many Citizens of Austin who have contributed to this effort. I am particularly grateful to Gail Vittori, Chip Wolfe, Michael Kuhn, Jana McCann, and Tom (Smitty) Smith for their thoughtful comments and editing aid.

Early on in this process, two groups were created. One was the Community of the Future/City of Austin group. This COFCOA group has met on a regular basis and will, I hope, continue to meet on a regular basis. It includes those in the City who are most knowledgeable of Sustainable and Efficiency technologies and Livability issues. They include Mark Kapner, Richard Morgan, Leslie Libby, Janna McCann, Fred Yebra, Fred Blood, Larry Alford, and Jerrel Gustafson,

Another group was composed mostly of Austin Citizens and called the Funnel Group. They include Bill Bunch, Bill Narum, Bruce Sterling, Charles Cirar, Charles H. Freeman, Chip Wolfe, Dana DeBeauvoir, Elizabeth Munger, Garry Mauro, Gary Vliet, Jane Pulaski, Jerry Harris, Jim Marston, John Hoffner, Kathryn

Houser, Kevin L. Conlin, Mark MacLeod, Michael Kuhn, Mike Sloan, Pete Parsons, Pliny Fisk, R E Smith, Richard Amato, Robin Schneider, Scot Sklar, Stacey Abel, Steve Jennings, and Tom Smith. Thank you all.

Finally, I thank Bill Narum for his excellent design and illustrations.

If we are to move forward... towards the building of a sustainable community, we must all acknowledge that our present situation is not.

We must acknowledge that our future is ours to make.

"There is one thing stronger than all the armies in the world, and that is an idea whose time has come."
Victor Hugo

Preface

By Roger Duncan

It is widely accepted that the pace of change in the world, our society, and our individual life is accelerating. In the developed world, the changes in business, social structures, and culture from just 50 years ago is dramatic. And 100-year comparisons seem like ancient history.

The electric utility industry did not exist just 100 years ago. Yet most of us just assume that large power plants, poles and wires running through the countryside and along our streets, and plugs and switches embedded in our buildings are the way we have always met our power needs — and will continue to meet those needs in the future. We do not realize that in historical terms the industry is a very recent phenomenon, and is very unlikely to remain in its current form as our society rushes into the new century.

A sustainable energy supply — clean, affordable, and reliable — is the very cornerstone of a sustainable society. This document is an attempt to discern that sustainable energy future, based on our best knowledge of current and future power technologies and environmental science.

I wanted this to be an accessible and enjoyable read for the people of Austin — especially those most interested in planning a sustainable city. That is why I wanted a writer to create the story — but a writer with the necessary energy and technical background. I was very fortunate that Michael Osborne was available for that task.

It is my hope that this book will stimulate the public discussion on what is possible in our energy future and inspire all of us to take the necessary step to actualize that sustainable vision.

Finally, and perhaps most importantly, I must stress that this is

A Comprehensive Energy Plan for the City, not The Comprehensive Energy Plan for the City or Austin Energy. The actual Comprehensive Energy Plan will be a living process developed over the course of many many years and many discussions.

This is the beginning of this process, not the end.

With that in mind, I must state that the material contained herein represents the opinion of the author and does not necessarily express the policy, position or views of the City of Austin or Austin Energy. This document is intended for educational and information purposes only.

Foreword

Why base a Community of the Future report describing a long-term comprehensive energy plan for the City of Austin on a personage from our Past?

Good Question.

Ben Franklin was one of the most extraordinary human beings the world has ever known. Born into the family of a Boston candle maker, Benjamin Franklin became the most famous American of his time. He helped found a new nation and defined the American character. He was a writer, inventor, diplomat businessman, musician, scientist, humorist, civic leader, international celebrity... genius.

Born January 17th in 1706, Ben Franklin was the youngest son of a youngest son of a youngest son of a youngest son. Peter the Great was the Czar of Russia. Europe was embroiled in War. Louis XIV sat on the throne in France. He was the Sun King.

James Watt, the inventor of the steam engine would not be born for another 30 years. Watt's invention, a practical steam engine, would not come for another 60 years.

In 1721, as Bach composed the Brandenburg Concerto, Franklin, age 15, was inventing swimming fins. At eighteen, he made his first of many trips to London just as Peter the Great was ending his reign. By the time George Washington was born, Franklin was publishing Poor Richard's Almanac. In 1750, he invented the lightning rod as the first coal mine in the colonies began operation. Ben Franklin believed that people volunteering together in a spirit of cooperation could accomplish great things. Driven by a strong sense of civic duty, he involved himself in his community and his nation. Always mindful of the "greater good," Franklin helped establish or improve institutions such as circulating libraries, public hospitals, mutual insurance companies, volunteer fire departments, agricultural colleges, and intellectual societies.

As a "man of science," Franklin is best known for his experiments with electricity, but his lifelong curiosity also led him to explore an amazing range of scientific topics. From the common cold to ocean currents, from medicine to music, and from agriculture to the aurora borealis, he believed that human logic could unlock the mysteries of the natural world. More interested in practical applications than in theory, Franklin put his ideas to work through such useful inventions as a smokeless fireplace, bifocal glasses, and the lightning rod.

He invented the armonica, the rocking chair, the street lamp, and white duck clothing used in tropical climates. He originated the first circulating library. He organized the first fire department, the modern post office system, and the first street-cleaning department.

He was the founder of the Democratic Party and the first political cartoonist.

He is the originator of Daylight Savings Time. He gave the first explanation of the Aurora Borealis. He discovered the Gulf Stream.

He was the first man to understand the nature of a cold. And, he was the first to discover that exhaled air is poisonous and thus originated the first system of ventilation.

He was the inventor of Plaster of Paris for fertilizing.

He is considered the father of modern dentistry.

Not only did he exercise his intelligence, he was the best swimmer of his time.

We usually think of Ben Franklin as an American patriot and founding father. But his influence extended much further. At a time when people rarely traveled more than 20 miles from where they were born, Franklin made eight Atlantic crossings and visited ten countries. As the first American Ambassador, he negotiated treaties with Great Britain, France, Germany, Sweden, and Spain and helped secure America's place in the world. As a respected scientist and scholar, he was granted honorary degrees in England, Scotland, and America. And, as an Enlightenment thinker, he exchanged letters with some of the greatest minds of the eighteenth century. A role model still today, Ben Franklin helped define "good citizenship."

Some have said that he was the first "civilized American."

By the time Franklin passed on in 1790, practically everything had changed. The Colonies were now the United States of America. The French National Assembly had written its own document extolling the Rights of Man just the year before. The Fall of the French King was now a matter of days.

When Franklin was well into middle age, the advent of the steam engine and the improvements in the mining of coal had laid the groundwork for another Revolution-The Industrial Revolution. In 1769, the first locomotive or steam carriage was demonstrated by the Frenchman Cugnot. The first operable steamship moved through the waters of the Potomac in 1786. The inventor, Rumsey, even demonstrated his work to George Washington.

If Ben Franklin was alive today, he might be a printer. But he would most likely have a web page with pithy sayings. He surely would have a weblog. He would probably have a computer that operated on his oral commands. He would be a pioneer in the new horizons of cyberspace just as he was a pioneer in the 1700's in printing, science, and philosophy.

He might have photovoltaics on his house and business and he would be expounding in his writings and lectures about the democratic virtues of distributed generation and solar energy. He would surely rail about the anti-democratic aspects of large-scale nuclear technology and the security risks such technology brings upon the people, as well as the burden it places on the generations that follow for it is they who will ultimately pay for its safe storage.

Given his understanding of optics and electricity, he probably would have been a solar inventor. He might invent a solar power plant that provides electricity at prices below 5cents/KWh. He would be tinkering with fuel cells and the electrolysis of water into hydrogen and oxygen.

As an Ambassador, he would recognize the inherent danger to a nation that was dependent on a foreign fuel. As a Statesman, he would be cautious to bring the horrible cause of War upon his people until all avenues of peace had proven to be unwise and incapable of success.

Franklin would insist that we as a Society and a Community move boldly towards a Solar-Hydrogen economy. Now.

In keeping with the belief that Franklin would have been at the vanguard of communications today, this document is not only printed and published on recycled paper, it is also included in a back pocket in the inside cover as an electronic document. The electronic document includes the hyperlinking that converts this document into an electronic vessel that can take you on a voyage into the world of energy, energy policy, climate change, transportation, renewable energy, hydrogen, and beyond.

Silver in the Mine, A Long Term Comprehensive Energy Plan for the City of Austin, unlike many public documents, is written to be enjoyed. Starting with the Introduction, the reader is given an overview of the history of electricity, the history and present generational makeup of Austin Energy, and the state of Public Power. Chapter One discusses our declining Oil and Gas Resources and Chapter Two discusses our deteriorating Environmental Resources. Chapter Three discusses Conservation, Green Building, and Renewables while Chapter Four addresses Transportation. Chapter Five is dedicated to a discussion of the New Technologies that are fast becoming mature strategies for meeting our needs.

Chapter Six is a detailed Plan consisting of Needs and Responses to those Needs. These elements represent the basic ingredients of the Plan. Each element is numbered suggesting the myriad elements and sub-elements that will need to be developed over the course of this process.

Chapter Seven is the "Get it for the Gipper" speech. It challenges us to move today towards our goal of a Sustainable Solar Hydrogen Economy. It offers a direction for The **Community of the Future.**

Contents

Silver in the Mine

A Long Term Comprehensive Energy Plan for the City of Austin

Recommendations

Overview

Community *of the* Future

Saving Nine

"A pessimist sees the difficulty in every opportunity; an optimist sees the opportunity in every difficulty."

Sir Winston Churchill

INTRODUCTION

The coming decades in the Electric Utility Industry will be full of surprises and changes. Spectacular breakthroughs in Technology may change the way we do everything. The results of War will not be known for some time. The effects of Climate Change may suddenly become incontrovertible and require our immediate and focused attention. Yet, within all of this uncertainty, lies certainty.

We know that we are depleting our finite resources of oil and gas.

We know that as we burn carbon fuels, that we add carbon to the atmosphere and thus augment the Greenhouse Effect. We know that this will cause serious disruption in one of the most significant assets we have as a civilization...A stable climate.

We know that many of our urban areas have air that is contaminated with pollution induced ozone and other particulates causing increased morbidity and loss of quality of life due to increased allergies and lung disease.

We know that in most challenges lies opportunity. It is that opportunity that is the focus of this document.

Austin Energy is one of the leading utilities in the country in its support of the environment and sustainable technologies. It has one of the leading, most popular "green choice" programs in the country. It has achieved over 400 MW in peak demand reduction through its conservation programs. Almost 100 MW of renewables are now part of the Utility's generation mix with more to come.

Austin Energy serves approximately 350,000 residential customers. By the year 2013, that number may be 450,000. In 25 years, there may be almost 700,000 residential customers who will require electric service. In 2002, about 3,700 GWhs of electricity were sold in the residential sector. Another 4,700 GWhs were sold in the commercial sector, and 1,700 GWhs flowed into the industrial sector. The total amount of electricity generated by the system in 2002 was more than 10,000 GWhs. By the year 2013, that number may be closer to 14,000 GWhs. In twenty-five years, Austin Energy may be providing 20,000 GWhs a year to its customers.

The current wave of deregulation in the Electric Utility arena provides a new landscape for Austin Energy (AE) to serve its Citizens. In this landscape, Municipal Utilities and Rural Electric Coops have the option to join the competitive environment if they choose to opt into it. Either way, deregulation offers new opportunities for Austin Energy to reinvent itself. Austin Energy can become even more of a leader in the field of sustainable energy and environmental expertise even in the new field of competition and so called "least cost" electricity.

In the future, Austin Energy will ultimately recharacterize itself. Is the electric utility in the business of providing electricity to run an air-conditioning unit or is it in the business of providing cool environments? Is the utility in the business of providing the electricity to run lights during the night or is it in the business of providing light? Should the utility provide fuel cells and solar systems to its customers? Should the utility expand into the transportation sector and provide electric or hybrid hydrogen cars through various purchasing and lease options?

All of these possibilities can be part of the operating ethic of Austin Energy now.

SUSTAINABILITY

It is the hope and the purpose of this Community of the Future effort that Austin Energy lead and direct this City into the future with this vision of a great city. That we, as Austin Citizens, will choose to make decisions which not only provide for the citizens who are alive now, but also for those that will be alive in twenty years or fifty years. Sustainability was defined by the United Nations Brundtland Commission in 1987 as "meeting the needs of the present without compromising the ability of future generations to meet their own needs."

Intergenerational equity cannot be met by markets which do not set aside resources for the future, or provide for the accounting of depleted natural resources. Free markets cause the cheapest, easiest to find resources to be consumed first. Sustainable Policies come from a deep understanding of the responsibility of the present generation to the generations that follow.

The Plan of this initiative is dedicated to the creation of a great city utility that has a deep understanding of this issue and this principle and to the well being of the future Citizens of this City.

FUEL

THE CONVENTIONAL VIEW

The executive summary of the World Energy Outlook states:

"The world has abundant reserves of energy. Proven energy reserves are adequate to meet demand until 2020 and well beyond." But there are two major problems with reserve estimates. They are biased for political reasons and they are biased because of tax or regulatory reasons.

This has given rise to a growing group of Contrarians. This handful of Hubbert Curve apostles and high paid consultants believe that the **peak of world oil production is going to occur in the middle of this decade.** They believe that world gas production will peak in around 2020.

Perhaps the most vocal and controversial of the Contrarians is Dr. Colin J Campbell. In his presentation on oil reserves and the ramifications of that potential he concludes:

Peak oil is a turning point for Mankind

· 100 years of easy growth ends

· Population peaks too for not unrelated reasons

· The transition to decline is a period of great tension

· Priorities shift to self-sufficiency and sustainability

· It may end up a better world

THE FUEL OF THE FUTURE

The Energy Information Agency shows that reserves of natural gas will grow over the next 20 years from 156 trillion cu. ft to approximately 175 trillion cu. ft. At consumption rates of 22 trillion/year, that is a 7-year reserve. For demand to grow and reserves to grow each year, more than 25 trillion cu. ft. of gas must be added to reserves annually. To avoid large imports from other countries, production must be increased above current levels.

Discovery in the early eighties from the US, Canada, and Mexico has dropped to less than 10 trillion cu. ft annually. Shifting this discovery record by 20 years indicates that natural gas production from the US will be substantially less than the 25 trillion cubic feet needed. These reserves will therefore be increased not by discovery but by the process of reevaluation or reserve growth. These re-evaluations are difficult to predict and quantify. Therefore, it can be inferred from these data, that large imports of natural gas will be required to meet the needs of the United States in the next twenty years.

TEXAS NATURAL GAS

Where will the natural gas for Texas power plants originate? Texas still has a surplus of natural gas production of about 2 trillion cu. ft. annually. Production is beginning to decline after a strong decade of production in the 90s. However, the US as a whole is now importing about 4 trillion cu.ft. Liquefied natural gas, the kind that can be placed in ships, has tripled in the last 3 years. Where will this gas originate? Russia has the largest reserves with 1705 trillion cu. ft. The entire Mid-East has about the same. Closer to the US, Venezuela has about the same as the US with Argentina coming in a far distant second. In Africa, Algeria and Nigeria have the largest reserves of natural gas with about 150 tcf each.

The World Energy Outlook published by the International Energy Agency states in its Executive Summary:

"The principal uncertainty in global energy supply prospects is cost. Advances in technology and productivity are driving production and transportation costs lower, but the depletion of the cheapest reserves and growing distances over which new supplies must be transported are, in many cases, pushing delivered energy costs up."

And the Outlook states:

"A number of technologies under consideration, or active, could radically alter the long-term supply picture. The main focus of current research on new supply technologies is hydrogen production and use. Hydrogen technology holds out the prospect of large-scale energy supply with minimal environmental impact.

Hydrogen production may be based on the electrolysis of water using nuclear or renewable energy."

THE ENVIRONMENT

CLIMATE CHANGE

The science of Climate Change may be assailable by its opponents. Indeed, there are serious holes in the International Panel on Climate Change (IPCC) and the World Meteorological Organization's (WMO) projections and models. These are the international organizations that were charged by the UN in 1988 to assess the scientific and technical literature on climate change. Their job is to predict the potential impacts of changes in climate, and evaluate options for the adaptation to and mitigation of climate change.

The Executive Summary of the most recent IPCC Report states:

"Virtually all sectors within North America are vulnerable to climate change to some degree. Although many sectors and regions are sensitive to climate change, the technological capability to adapt to climate change is readily available for the most part. Even when current adaptive capability has been factored in, long-lived natural forest ecosystems in the east and interior west; water resources in the southern plains; agriculture in the southeast and southern plains; human health in areas currently experiencing diminished urban air quality; northern ecosystems and habitats; estuarine beaches in developed areas; and low-latitude cold-water fisheries will remain among the most vulnerable sectors and regions."

What does this mean for those of us in Central Texas? We may see changes in the amount of water in the Colorado River. That will affect our water supply. We may see less rain and when it comes, it will come in larger events making floods more likely. The ground will be dryer because of the increased evaporation. Water tables may drop.

Our electric bills will go up in the summer unless we make our homes and the equipment in them more efficient.

On the positive side, winters will get milder and milder. There will be other bonuses with climate change- like longer growing seasons and the potential of increased plant growth from the heavier concentration of CO_2. Many of them may end up providing significant positive economic impact.

AIR QUALITY

Like any other large city whose transportation base is the car, Air quality in Austin gets worse each year. It has been estimated that bad air kills or accelerates the deaths of 50,000 Americans every year. About that many Americans die each year in automobile accidents.

In Austin, although statistics are not available, it can be inferred from these morbidity rates that 250 Austinites will fall victim prematurely to bad air every year. Those Austinites who suffer from chronic allergies exacerbated by bad air dwarf that number.

There is relatively little that the City of Austin can do to change the Change in the weather. True, we can characterize our actions as a very small piece of a very large pie towards climate stabilization. Even a major move to sustainable energy sources probably will not change the future we have already cast for ourselves. It will change the future for the generations that follow us though.

The massive deployment and use of these technologies and strategies will leave us with something we do have control over. It will give us CLEAN AIR.

CONSERVATION AND RENEWABLES

EFFICIENCY

The American economy has made substantial improvements in efficiency over the past 30 years. In 1973 it took 19,000 BTUs to produce one dollar of GNP. Today that ratio is closer to 11,000 BTUs to one dollar of GNP. Yet the nations of Western Europe and Japan are almost twice as efficient. This ratio is important.

If energy costs 2 dollars per 100,000 BTUs (7 cents/KWh), then every dollar of GNP requires 22 cents of energy. It is a large constituent in the costs of the goods we, as a nation, sell to ourselves and others.

CONSERVATION IN AUSTIN

In 2001, it is estimated that Austin Energy's Conservation Programs achieved a reduction in overall system demand of 45 megawatts in required power plant capacity. Total energy saved in 2001 from this increase in conservation is estimated to be over 54 thousand MWhs. The combined effect of all of Austin Energy's Conservation Programs will save over 600 GWhs this year. That means that the combined effect of Austin Energy's conservation efforts is equivalent to one large coal plant. That plant has been avoided without the loss of convenience or comfort. Indeed, what has been avoided is the pollution, the loss of real estate to generation, and the depletion of a finite resource. One less coal plant is a significant accomplishment.

ZERO ENERGY BUILDINGS (ZEB)

A zero net energy home generates more power than it uses at peak demand. During times of power outage, the home generates its own power or runs on its own energy storage thus providing the homeowner essential energy security. This potential was demonstrated in 1998 by the Florida Solar Energy Center. In their Lakeland project, two identical homes were built with the same floor plan on nearby lots. The control home conformed to local building practices and codes. The other was designed with a maximum concern for energy efficiency and the implementation of solar technology. Both homes were approximately 2400 square feet in size.

At 5:00 p.m. on June 18th, the utility experienced its annual summer peak demand. In fact, it was the hottest daytime temperatures ever recorded in Lakeland. The Zero Energy home produced more energy than it consumed at 4:30 and 5:30. During the course of the day, the Zero Energy home consumed a remarkable

199 watt hours of utility supplied power. At 8 cents/KWh, that is about 1.5 cents.

During this peak day, the ZEB over a 24 hour period used 72% less power for air-conditioning **and** it maintained cooler indoor temperatures than the control home. According to the FSEC, 29% of these savings were delivered by the high efficiency AC, high performance windows delivered 19% of the savings, the white tile roof was responsible for 16%, and the oversized interior ducts produced 14 % of the savings. Duct tightness contributed another 8%. The 3-foot overhangs provided 7%, while the R10 walls saved 4%, and overall house tightness saved 3%.

RENEWABLE ENERGY

Today, through its purchases and many other installations, the Austin Energy mix of resources includes almost 100 Megawatts of renewable energy. Most of this comes from a wind facility on a great mesa in West Texas that overlooks the Pecos River. In 1999, the Austin City Council resolved that 5% of Austin's electric generation capacity should come from Renewables by 2005. Austin Energy is on track to accomplish that goal on time.

TRANSPORTATION

Transportation shapes Cities. But not only does transportation shape cities, energy policy shapes cities. And this country does have an energy policy. The policy is inexpensively priced energy. Inexpensively priced gasoline creates flat, spread out cities that use even more energy.

Each person in the US averages around 10,870 km of city driving a year. Compare this with Western Europe averages of less than 5,000 and averages of less than 2,000 km in developed Asia. In Western Europe, 42% of the people drive to work or wherever, 39% use public transport, and 18% walk or cycle to work. In developed Asia, 20% drive a car, 60% use public transport, and 20% walk or cycle. The averages in the US are strikingly different.

In the US, 86% drive, 9% use public transit, and less than 5% walk or cycle.

Some studies now indicate that the real costs of automobile dependence outweigh the economic benefits of car transportation. Real estate analysts have come to see that denser cities that have alternatives to the car are better investment bets than sprawling suburban areas.

In Austin, 99% of transportation CO_2 emissions come from private vehicles and air travel. Public transport is less than 1%. Those of us who walk or bicycle to work number slightly more than 10,000 according to the Census Bureau. Of the one half million workers, that would mean 2% use human power to get there. Western European cities have almost 20%. Public ridership in Austin is less than 40,000 a day. That is slightly less than the US average and 1/4 of the European city average.

Here in Austin, if you have ever attended a debate on light rail or any discussion on mass transportation, one thing is for sure. These people know what they are talking about and they are very committed to their ideas and positions. Unfortunately, they don't agree. In the Light Rail debate in Austin, the phrase "Costs too much, Does too little" decimated the pro Rail advocates in the last election.

THE UNIFIED ENERGY SYSTEM

Why are the two systems, our transportation power system and our electrical power system "noncompatible"? It's as if one is a Mac and the other is a PC.

A unified energy system would allow homeowners to power their homes with their cars by charging up battery banks. Such a house would not only be self-sufficient, it would have numerous powering options. Solar powered homes with a unified energy strategy could reduce the size of the photovoltaic array and/or omit back-up generation.

All electric vehicles achieve this unification. Whether the vehicle uses batteries or fuel cells is a non-issue on this strategic issue. The systems can and should be unified. Unification will reduce costs by reducing society's total investment. It will increase reliability. It will create a better market. It will provide an avenue for independence.

TELECOMMUTING

As much as we say we would like to work at home, most telecommuters feel isolated when they don't come into the office. This can be replaced somewhat with sophisticated video conferencing, video e-mail, and screen sharing, and more sophisticated conferencing programs that provide for more group interaction through split screening.

The Austin Carbon Dioxide Reduction Strategy Update estimates that less than 10,000 workers telecommute. This number could be dramatically increased. A study by Apogee concludes that 10% of the work force could be telecommuting. That would represent 50,000 workers. The aggressive scenario found in the CO2 report assumes 85,000 telecommuters. This kind of acceptance would reduce CO2 emissions by more than 170,000 tons a year. Advanced telecommuting could make this number even higher.

TECHNOLOGY REVIEW OF NEW TECHNOLOGIES
WIND

In the span of 20 years, wind technology has grown from house size units of 25 KW to utility scale units of 2.5 MW. A farmer can put in a field of 25 or 50 KW machines but 1 MW machines require cranes, lawyers, and interconnect agreements. As it has matured, the wind industry has become a utility scale business. Today the price of wind with federal production credits is less than 3 cents. That is below the utility fuel costs of many natural gas plants. Indeed, two gas plants in Texas are now running as load following units that work in tandem with the wind facilities that surround them. It is cheaper to run the wind than to run the gas plant.

The growth of the wind industry in the United States and the world is truly impressive. Wind Power is the fastest growing source of electrical power there is. The web sites of the American Wind Energy Association and the European Wind Energy Association tell their stories well.

SOLAR ENERGY

The PV industry, like the Wind industry, is beginning to mature.

In determining the wisdom of any technology that is to be deployed on a large scale, the concept of energy recapture must be considered. It simply makes no sense to embrace a technology that cannot capture and deliver more usable energy than it takes to create it.

In the early days of the oil boom, this ratio of "energy returned" to "energy invested" was over 30 to 1. Today, that ratio is closer to 10 to 1. Wind turbines are now providing energy returns in that same range. Consequently, the prices for wind-generated electricity are competitive with the fossil market.

Currently, crystalline PV technologies have energy ratios that range from a low of 2 to 1 to a high of about 4 to 1. Thin film technologies range in the area of 5 to 1. Once 10 to 1 ratios are achieved, large-scale deployment of PV can be considered. Multi-sun strategies have the potential to increase the energy ratio beyond the 10 to 1 threshold.

The National Renewable Energy Lab predicts that PV costs will approach one dollar/Watt in the next 10 years. If this prediction is correct, Distributed Solar Energy for electrical generation will become a viable option.

Solar Energy Generation Stations are capable now of producing electricity in the 9 to 10 cent range. With a national commitment, large-scale solar plants could be competitive today in the 5 to 7 cent range. Technologies which employ unique solar strategies such as power towers and hemispheric moving focus can produce bulk power economically, and exhibit highly favorable energy ratios approaching 10 to 1.

Austin Energy should take the lead in developing these technologies, not only for its stockholder/citizens, but also for markets and utilities outside of the Austin area. An Austin Energy advanced in these technologies would be capable of maximizing its own resources and profitability. Such profitability could actually reduce rates for Citizens while providing a long-term sustainable strategy.

BIOGAS and BIOMASS

Biomass can and could provide the fuel for our electrical needs. But, it takes a large area to provide large amounts of fuel. Providing a third of Austin Energy's fuel through biomass would require approximately 130,000 acres. That area of 200 square miles is roughly the size of Austin. To provide the same amount of energy with solar would require 4,000 acres. To provide the energy through wind plants would require 22,000 acres.

According to the SEDC Renewable Energy Assessment Report, Texas has 250 quads of solar energy that is accessible, 4 quads of wind energy, 3 quads of biomass, 1 quad each of water and geothermal and 1/4 of a quad in building climatology.

Presently, Texas consumes 12 quads of energy. Half of that is consumed by Industry. Three quads are used in the electric sector and 2 1/2 quads are used in the transportation sector.

BIOENERGY

Other life forms besides plants can be used to provide usable energy. Some bacteria can provide an electric current that can act to break water into hydrogen and oxygen. There are nanobacteria that could be used in creating biocells for electrical production. Anaerobic digesters can convert food and animal waste into methane. Many bio-energy operating systems are in their infancy.

FUEL CELLS AND MICROTURBINES

Some companies like Plug Power hope to provide fuel cells for the home that operate outside the home much like a standard air-conditioner unit. Other companies like Ballard are working on transportation applications.

A reversible fuel cell that provides energy on peak and stores off peak energy as hydrogen and oxygen would be of maximum value to an electric utility that wishes to make the most out of its renewable resources and existing generation assets.

Microturbines are a new type of combustion turbine being used for stationary energy generation applications. They are small combustion turbines, approximately the size of a refrigerator, with outputs of 25 KW to 500 KW, and can be located on sites with space limitations for power production.

Microturbines are very fuel price sensitive. At natural gas prices below 2.00 mcf, electricity from microturbines can be produced for around 10 cents/KWh. At prices above 6.00/mcf, generation costs run in the same range as solar photovoltaics.

Microturbines could run relatively cleanly on hydrogen.

HYDROGEN

There are more than just a few energy visionaries who seem to see the post-carbon future- that Future is the Solar Hydrogen Energy System. Hydrogen can be used in any application in which fossil fuels are being used today, with the sole exception of cases in which carbon is specifically needed. Hydrogen can be used as a fuel in furnaces, internal combustion engines, turbines and jet engines, even more efficiently than fossil fuels, i.e., coal, petroleum and natural gas. Automobiles, buses, trains, ships, submarines, airplanes and rockets can run on hydrogen. Hydrogen can also be converted directly to electricity by fuel cells, with a variety of applications in transportation and stationary power generation.

The simplicity and universality of a hydrogen economy is more than appealing. The issue of efficiency is important, but we are not talking about a finite resource here. If a large 5-megawatt wind turbine can produce electricity for 2 cents/KWh and the hydrogen energy it produces can be shipped for a fraction of that to a fuel cell or turbine which is 90 % efficient, the 80% efficiency of the electrolysis process is acceptable. If the built environment is composed of nanoconducting PV paints that produce electricity at 1 cent/KWh, do we care if hydrogen carries 1/3 the energy per unit of volume of methane? The total cost of the KWh is still less than the current cost and there is no pollution or depletion.

The marriage of hydrogen and electricity will provide Earth with an energy system that is clean, sustainable, and equitable.

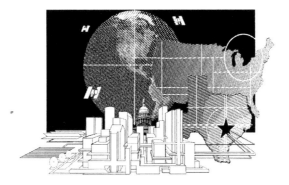

THE PLAN

We must identify or develop what we need, confirm that it will work, and deploy our findings and developments effectively and economically. These stages will be known as Project Matrix, The Probus Program, and Actus. Each program will consider the transportation sector, the building sector, and the electric sector. In many cases, these sectors will necessarily overlap. The unification of the transportation and electric sectors is an obvious example. Zero energy buildings will involve both buildings and electric. Land use planning will involve all three of these areas. Mass transportation will necessarily involve land use planning, buildings, transportation, and electric.

To SUCCEED we will need the following:

We will need a strong endorsement by the Citizens of Austin.

We will need a Council and a Mayor willing and capable of implementing that endorsement.

We must have an Austin Energy that continues to follow through and define itself along the lines of its existing mission statement while embracing a new vision that maximizes the potential of Austin Energy.

We will need to receive the full cooperation from all the relevant departments of the federal government and the state government.

We will need the cooperation of our neighboring cities, the county, and the surrounding counties.

We will need the cooperation of the business community and the educational community.

And, we will need to be united.

THE ELECTRIC SECTOR

Austin Energy is the key and the door to obtaining the vision of a truly sustainable city. Austin Energy and its management will have to whole-heartedly embrace this task. It will need to grow a new skin and leave the old one behind. Management will need to craft a new vision statement that captures the potential of Austin Energy and the imagination of the Citizens of Austin. It will need to craft a vision statement that redefines Austin Energy as a provider of energy and service. That energy might come as cooling, or heat, communication services, or even transportation. In order to become a leader in the protection of the environment, our vision must include the development of the sustainable technologies that will be required to provide that protection.

To accomplish our goal, we must have a plan to meet our growth and we must have a plan to replace our existing generation with sustainable alternatives. To become a sustainable city, we should look at all of our plants and plans- past, present, and future, with an eye for how they will fit into a vision of sustainability and a future solar-hydrogen economy. At present growth rates, it can be imagined that our generation needs will double in the next twenty-five years. In order to have a sustainable utility and city, we must build 2500 new megawatts and convert the existing 2500 megawatts in the same time frame.

NEW GENERATION

To meet the needs of AE's growth sustainably, a combination of new bulk power plants, distributed generation, and future unification with the transportation sector will be employed. Resources will come from the sun, the wind, biomass, geothermal, and other forms of renewable energy. Hydrogen and electricity will be the energy carriers that unify the system. Advanced emerging technologies should be considered.

THE UTILITY OF THE FUTURE

The Sustainable Utility of the Future will look very different from the Utility of Today.

Unlike the present day utility, the Utility of the Future would be a balance of centralized and distributed technologies. To quote the EPRI Technology Roadmap, "Revolutionary advancements appear likely in the field of distributed generation over the next 10 years and beyond. As these technologies are developed, small-scale distributed generation and storage systems can become valuable new elements of the distributed utility of the future."

Rather than meeting load growth in large lumpy acquisitions of 500 MWs or more, the Utility of the Future will be able to grow its ability to meet the needs of its customers as its customer base grows.

The Utility of the Future will experience more and more decarbonization. Quoting EPRI's Roadmap, "Considerable energy decarbonization progress has occurred over the last two centuries, facilitated to an ever greater degree in this century by electricity. In the early part of the 19th century, wood yielded in time to coal, and in this century to oil and natural gas-each with progressively less carbon per unit of energy. Decarbonization has made further inroads with the introduction of nuclear and commercial renewable energy. This progress, if maintained through technology advancement, puts the world on a predictable trajectory toward a clean, electricity and hydrogen based energy economy.

"As the world economy electrifies, coal and oil can drop from more than 60% of the global energy mix today to the margin by 2100. In the past, decarbonization has occurred as a natural outcome of the economic drive for cost reduction and efficiency improvement. In the future, the economic drivers will be supplemented by environmental concerns related to Global Greenhouse Gas emissions and other pollutants from fossil fuels."

THE SUSTAINABLE UTILITY

Depending on which strategy emerges from the Matrix and which technology proves superior in Probus, the right strategy of resources and technologies can be employed to assure that Austin Energy is a leader in environmental stewardship and the best community based electric utility that it can be.

Moving towards a decarbonized sustainable utility may ultimately prove to be the new conservative approach of the successful Electric Utility of The Future in this age of change.

As the EPRI road map states:

"Sustainability tomorrow requires our urgent commitment today."

THE TRANSPORTATION SECTOR

THE UNIFIED TRANSPORTATION SYSTEM

"The inherently underutilized storage and power generation capacities of new hybrid electric vehicles could be connected to serve residential and commercial building loads", states the EPRI roadmap. "During the majority of time when vehicles are not being operated, they could provide an extensive distributed power generation and storage network. If, for example, one million such vehicles were on the road in the year 2010, they could contribute 50-100 GW of generating capacity, or about 5 to 10% of anticipated US capacity."

If these vehicles or Personal Transportation Devices were fueled by hydrogen or electrically powered by sustainable resources and yet capable of being part of an overall larger transportation strategy and infrastructure, our cities could see the end of the pollution and air degradation they currently must abide.

TELETRANSPORTATION

Telework could substantially change the amount of traffic on our rush hour freeways. It can certainly be used as an agent to reschedule the workday to reduce traffic congestion.

Telework neighborhood centers with childcare can make substantial changes in the way we work and our need to transport our bodies when it is often our ideas and creativity that need to be transported. Much of our transportation may be replaced by advanced software that allows the virtual workplace to compete with the actual workplace.

BUILDINGS

ZERO ENERGY BUILDINGS

With the advancement of materials and knowledge, our buildings will become smarter and more independent. They will become entities to themselves much like large robots. They will be able to respond to weather before it comes. They will provide their own energy. They may collect their own water. They will heat that water. They will recycle that water and their other waste streams.

Zero Energy Buildings will allow the Utility of the Future and the Community of the Future to grow naturally. They are the Future.

NEVER LEAVE THAT TILL TOMORROW
WHAT YOU CAN DO TODAY

We do not face an energy crisis.

We face a crisis of consciousness.

The Universe is not about to run out of energy. There is energy everywhere. In fact, as Einstein predicted and Oppenheimer proved, mass itself is energy. We are at the end of a very long road. Starting with gathered wood, then moving to peat and coal, to whale oil and plant oils, to rock oil and its sister natural gas, we have steadily developed in the art of using energy. Humankind's great adventure of converting from the present carbon, fire burning age we now know, to an age where the radiant energy that exists all around is transformed to usable energy, is upon us now. We have only to recognize our condition and act responsibly.

In the next few decades, humankind will no longer need to burn carbon. We will more likely use the carbon we have placed in the air to build with that carbon through nanotechnology. We will no longer take resources out of the ground and smelt them like we did at the beginning of the Iron Age. We will no longer burn coal to make steam to drive an engine like we did at the beginning of the Industrial Age. We will no longer adhere to a belief that we must suffer a little bit of pollution if we are to prosper. We will understand with our computers and with our interface with these and other tools of the mind and of control that many of the beliefs that were held to be true during the height of the age of carbon were true only during the Age of Carbon.

As computers and humans become more and more integrated, we will truly see new horizons in the biosciences, in medicine, in physics, in our understanding of the universe, and our place in it. We will know and understand that the universe is full of energy.

And we will know and understand the abundance we have been given.

THE COMMUNITY OF THE FUTURE

It may seem a little presumptuous, if not a little silly to think that Austin will become a truly great community. Yet, we know there is no way to be great except by trying to be great. Austin is uniquely situated in the State, in the Country, and in the World to emerge as a great Community.

There is a growing critical mass here in Austin that can create a clean energy scene that marries the style of a community that loves music and art with a community that embraces the realities and potential of the technologies of the future.

Thomas Freidman, of the New York Times, has called for this country to make a commitment to the development of renewable energy similar to the commitment that we made in World War II. He suggests that we begin a <u>Manhattan style project</u> to develop another energy system that is independent of the present energy system and its dependence on foreign oil and foreign natural gas.

Here in Austin, we can forge a nexus of University assets with the assets found in our semiconductor and software companies with the assets of a well-educated Citizenry. We have an electric utility that has the best green building program, the best efficiency programs, and the best green pricing program for clean energy in the country.

We have the potential to lead the World in providing the new technologies that the World will need. Hardly anyone who knows or cares about the Future will not know about Austin, Texas.

For it is **The Community of the Future.**

"All this will not be finished in the first 100 days.
Nor will it be finished in the first 1,000 days,
nor in the life of this Administration,
nor even perhaps in our lifetime on this planet.
But let us begin."

John Fitzgerald Kennedy

Introduction

The Austin Energy Almanack

Electric

"Life's tragedy is that we get old too soon and wise too late."

Benjamin Franklin

THE PAST

When Benjamin Franklin went out into the rain to fly his kite in the thunderstorm, more than just a few of his neighbors thought him to be a little bit on the eccentric side. Benjamin Franklin didn't invent electricity anymore than Edison, but he did play an important part in making this mysterious force the everyday part of our world that it is today.

In 1747, Benjamin Franklin in America and William Watson (1715-87) in England independently reached the same conclusion: all materials possess a single kind of electrical "fluid" that can penetrate matter freely but that can be neither created nor destroyed. The action of rubbing merely transfers the fluid from one body to another, electrifying both. Franklin and Watson originated the principle of conservation of charge: the total quantity of electricity in an insulated system is constant.

Franklin defined the fluid, which corresponded to vitreous electricity, as positive and the lack of fluid as negative. Therefore, according to Franklin, the direction of flow was from positive to negative—the opposite of what is now known to be true. A subsequent two-fluid theory was developed, according to which samples of the same type attract, whereas those of opposite types repel.

Franklin was acquainted with the Leyden jar, a glass jar coated inside and outside with tinfoil. It was the first capacitor, a device used to store charge. The Leyden jar could be discharged by touching the inner and outer foil layers simultaneously, causing an electrical shock to a person. If a metal conductor was used, a spark could be seen and heard. Franklin wondered whether lightning and thunder were also a result of electrical discharge. During a thunderstorm in 1752, Franklin flew a kite that had a metal tip. At the end of the wet, conducting hemp line on which the kite flew he attached a metal key, to which he tied a nonconducting silk string that he held in his hand. The experiment was extremely hazardous, but the results were unmistakable: when he held his knuckles near the key, he could draw sparks from it. The next two who tried this extremely dangerous experiment were killed.

The possibility that electricity does not consist of a smooth, continuous fluid probably occurred to many scientists. Even Franklin once wrote that the "fluid" consists of "particles extremely subtile."

Nevertheless, a great deal of evidence had to be accumulated before the view was accepted that electricity comes in tiny, discrete amounts, looking not at all like a fluid when viewed microscopically. James Clerk Maxwell opposed this particle theory. Toward the end of the 1800s, however, the work of Sir Joseph John Thomson (1856-1940) and others proved the existence of the electron.

This view of matter, still considered correct in many ways, established the electrical force as that which holds an atom together. After Rutherford presented his atom, the Danish physicist Niels Bohr proposed that the electrons have only certain orbits about the nucleus and that other orbits are impossible.

Early in the 20th century the quantum theory was developed. According to this theory, the electron is a smeared cloud of mass and charge. In some situations the electron cloud might be so small that the particle appears to be much like the tiny, charged marble of earlier views. In other situations, such as when the electron is in an atomic orbit, the cloud is many times larger.

Today, 250 years after Benjamin Franklin conducted his experiments, electricity is commonplace and essential to advanced civilization. Excepting those who make it their vocation, hardly anyone really understands it. Yet, only a few of us are afraid to plug the stereo in. Some of us still stick a fork in the toaster and bathe with the hair dryer on the ledge. Darwin is doing the work on that.

The early days of electrical generation were wild. Linemen were lost like coalminers. But, they didn't have the luxury of canaries. Working for the electric utility was a very dangerous job. Today, Austin Energy is a safe workplace providing reliable electricity to 370,000 customers. Austin Energy is the Tenth largest Public Power Utility in the United States. The combined generating capacity is 2600 Megawatts. In 2002, the peak demand was approximately 2400 Megawatts.

It is not necessary to understand the physics of electricity to use your hair dryer, and it is not necessary to understand electrical units of measurement to discuss energy policy or the politics of power, but it really helps. It's disconcerting, if not downright disturbing to hear college-educated professionals discussing electrical issues constantly confusing energy with power. In the words of the humorist, energy is how long you can go into the night; power is whether or not it makes a difference. Actually, the concept is relatively easy to express. Energy is power times time.

POWER AND ENERGY

The basic unit of measurement for quantifying electricity is the Watt. Named after James Watt, this unit measures power. If you multiply it by a unit of time such as an hour, you get energy. One watt is not much power. Most light bulbs are 60 watts. The fancy energy saving bulbs use 10 or 15 watts but they give the light (measured in things called lumens) of a 60-watt bulb. Run a

60-watt bulb for an hour and you get 60 watt/hours. Do that all day and you have 1.44 KWhs. At 7 cents per KWh, that would cost about a dime. Do that all month and you've spent about three dollars.

One Watt for one second is the same amount of energy you would find in one Joule. That's not quite the amount of power you could expect to get from your favorite CD if it was a solar cell. (1.5 Watts) One British Thermal Unit is the amount of energy it takes to raise one pound of water one degree F. If you understand that Amps times Volts equals Watts, and that Watts times hours equals Whs, you can pretty much figure out anything.

A KWh is 1000 watt hours. It is 3,600,000 Joules. It is the energy from 100 square feet of photovoltaics in an hour. (or 10 sq. ft. on a long summer day). It is 3414 BTUs. It's the amount of energy needed to raise 41 gallons of water by 10 degrees. If you assume the water coming in to your hot water heater is 70 degrees and you raise your 40-gallon tank by 50 degrees, it takes 5 KWhs or about 40 cents. Curiously enough, a KWh is also the same amount of energy present in a 3000-pound car traveling 160 miles per hour! It's also the same amount of energy in a 60-pound lead acid battery or the battery in a very large American car. (Such as an SUV)

So that's the KWh. And that's the way most of us pay for electricity. Most rates for electricity are around 7 to 9 cents, depending on where you live and how much of it you buy. Californians and New Yorkers pay over a dime. Here in Austin we pay around 8 cents, depending on how much the utility is paying for the natural gas that they are burning in their natural gas turbines and boilers. You would think there would be long-term contracts, but they are generally not available. The utility passes the cost directly on to us, the consumers. From time to time that fuel price adjustment goes up or down.

AUSTIN ENERGY

The utility known as Austin Energy had humble beginnings. It

was born on May 5th, 1890, when Austin voters approved bonds
funding a dam across the Colorado River, an electric powerhouse,
and a delivery system. (Water service was also approved.)

Five years later the first electricity was produced. Five years
after that, the dam was destroyed and eight workers were
drowned when the powerhouse flooded. A week later, power
was resumed utilizing old equipment including two generators
salvaged from the river bottom. Thirty-five years later, the Flood
of 35 takes the City's only power plant off line. A tie to Texas
Power and Light from east Austin brings in temporary power to
the City, but the Utility is not fully functional for another six months.

After barely surviving the depression, the Utility interconnected
with another utility, the Lower Colorado River Authority. That
was the first year without a blackout.

In 1949, the first two generating units at Seaholm became operational.
Walter Seaholm had saved the utility after the early flood by
operating the utility more efficiently than the competition could.
In 1960, the Holly plant came on line. Two years later, the first
bucket truck was acquired. (What did they use?) Ten years later,
the Decker Plant became operational. Two years after, Austin
voters did not approve the bonds to purchase a portion of the
South Texas Nuclear Project (STNP.)

Then, in 1973, after a war in the Mideast, an oil embargo, and
turned-off Christmas lights, Austin voters approve 161 million in
revenue bonds for a 16% interest in the STNP. In 1979, Austinites
authorize more money for the STNP. The same year, our first coal
plant, the Fayette Power Plant, comes on line. The next year, the
second unit comes on line giving Austin 570 MW of new generation.
The total of 1140 MW is shared with the LCRA.

The year after that, in 1981, Austin voters authorize the City
Council to sell Austin's 16% share in the nuclear plant. The
Council is unable to do so. And Austin politics would never be
the same. One year later, the appliance efficiency program is
launched. Two years after that, the American Public Power

Association recognizes Austin as a leader in conservation and renewable energy. In 1984, the conservation power plant concept is unveiled. In 1986, the largest solar plant in Texas, the PV 300 solar plant, is dedicated just a year after Austin receives a 120 million dollar settlement from Brown and Root for the cost overruns on STNP. Four years later, the nuclear plant becomes fully operational and Austin residents begin to take advantage of the city's 400 MW of generation from the facility. Still, only a year later, the STNP owners file suit against Westinghouse for equipment deficiencies. The same year, the electric utility department receives the National Environmental Awards Council's Environmental Achievement Award.

Throughout the 90s, the department continued to become more and more sensitive and responsive to the needs of its citizens and the environment by building more solar plants and by participating in the first major wind project in Texas with the LCRA and Texas General Land Office. Meanwhile, STNP is shut down for a year to address deficiencies cited by the NRC.

Today, Austin Energy is one of the leading utilities in the country in its support of the environment and sustainable technologies. It has one of the leading, most popular green choice programs in the country. It has a solar explorer program where homeowners receive PV installations on their roofs. It has achieved over 400 MW in peak demand reduction through its conservation programs. Over 35 thousand metric tons of carbon dioxide are reduced annually through these programs. Almost 100 MW of renewables are now part of the Utility's generation mix with more to come. Council's resolution of 5% of total generation from Renewable Energy by 2005 is on schedule to be met as new wind contracts come on line.

Austin Energy serves approximately 350,000 residential customers. By the year 2013, that number may be 450,000 if current growth continues. In 25 years, there may be almost 700,000 residential customers who will require electric service. Perhaps 3,700 GWhs of electricity will be sold to these residents in 2002. Another

4,700 GWhs will be sold in the commercial sector, and 1,700 GWhs will go into the industrial sector. The total amount of electricity generated by the system will be more than 10,000 GWhs. By the year 2013, that number may be closer to 14,000 GWhs. In twenty-five years, Austin Energy may be providing 20,000 GWhs a year to its customers.

In the residential sector approximately 66% of the sales will be to single-family residences and 33% of the sales will be made to multi-family units.

On the Commercial Energy side, less than half of the energy sold will go to retail businesses, 37% will be sold to offices, and schools will take about 5%.

From its rather modest beginnings, Austin Energy is now an organization of over 1400 full time employees with an annual gross income of over 750 million dollars. That's more than one half million dollars income for each employee. The current inventory of generation includes:

Project	Installation Dates	Net Capacity
Holly (gas/oil) - 4 units	1960-74	570 MW
Decker (gas/oil) - 2 units	1970-77	770 MW
Fayette (coal) - 2 units	1979-80	600 MW
Decker (gas turbine) - 4 units	1988	200 MW
South Texas Project		
(Nuclear) - 2 units	1988-89	400 MW
Renewables (wind/landfill/solar)	1986-2001	101 MW
Sand Hill (gas)	2001	180 MW
	2004	300 MW
Total		3,121 MW
System Peak Demand:		2,383 MW

INTO THE FUTURE

The current wave of deregulation in the Electric Utility arena

In this landscape, Municipal Utilities such as AE, and Coops have the option to join the competitive environment if they choose to opt into it. The Texas Legislature can always change this landscape. But for now, the decision for the City of Austin to join the competitive market can be made by the Council and by the Citizens who elect them as their proxy. No matter which we choose, deregulation offers new opportunities for Austin Energy to reinvent itself. Austin Energy can become even more of a leader in the field of sustainable energy and environmental expertise even in the new field of competition and so called "least cost" electricity.

Public Power has an impressive record of providing electricity to its citizens at rates that are less than investor owned utilities. According to The US Energy Information Agency, residential customers of the Public Power Utilities nationwide paid 16% less than the average residential customers of the Investor Owned Utilities. The average rate for PPU was 7.3 cents/KWh and the average rate for IOUs was 8.5/KWh. The average residential customer of a Public Power Utility pays less than the average customer of a Coop who pays 7.6 cents/KWh. The same is true for the average commercial customer. The Industrial customer fairs better with IOUs where the rates are equal to Public Power rates. Coops offer the best rates to industrial customers. (They support cotton gins, etc.). In Texas, the residential rates for Public Power average 7.6 cents and the rates for Investor Owned Utilities average 8.1 cents. Texas Coops have residential rates averaging 7.8 cents/KWh. In Alaska, the averages for Public Power vs. IOU power are 11.1 and 13.3. In Idaho, the rates are 4.4 and 5.4 cents/KWh. In New York, the respective rates are 12.1 and 14.6. In California they are 9.9 and 11.1. The average rate in Austin is 7.8 cents/KWh.

Two things are clear; rates in Texas and in Austin are good. Residential customers generally do better with Public Power. Industrial customers do better with Investor Owned Utilities. That makes for a lively community dialogue. Large employers will campaign to move towards open market competition where they can improve their bottom line by reducing energy costs, while their employees will most likely be able to meet their household budgets better without it.

The New York Power Authority is the largest Public Power Utility in the country with 48,000 GWhs sold. The Los Angeles system is half its size and is number three in the country after the Salt River Project in Arizona. San Antonio is number six in the country at 18,000 GWhs and Austin is number 20 at just over 10,000 GWhs sold. The Lower Colorado River Authority is 14th at around 12,500 GWhs. LCRA and Austin together would be the number four Public Power Utility in the country, just behind LA.

From the point of view of customers, LA is number one, San Antonio is number five, and Austin is 10th. From the point of view of generation, New York is number one, San Antonio is number four, LA is 6th and Austin is 13th. LCRA, San Antonio, and Austin together generate over 40,000 GWhs annually. Together, these three systems are the largest public power utility in the country.

The largest by revenue is the LA system with over 2 1/2 Billion in dollars collected. Austin, LCRA, and San Antonio collect just a little less. If the LCRA was not just a wholesale authority, its revenues would be greater than the $560 million it collects today and the combined total of these three Central Texas public power utilities would be greater than the largest in the Country.

Obviously, there is a large amount of Public Power in Central Texas.

Senate Bill 7, the Texas law that deregulates electric utilities, allows the public power utilities to join the competitive market if they choose. Will these utilities opt to join in competition?

And what will that mean to residential rates?

Perhaps the landscape could change substantially. Could the LCRA and Austin Energy someday become a single entity? Will the City Council someday opt to give Austin Energy a board and governance similar to the one that is employed in San Antonio?

There are many possibilities.

<u>Austin Energy</u> can continue now to move forward to protect and serve its Citizens. It can move forward to protect its Citizens from higher fuel prices by continuing to purchase wind power at rates that are known over the long term instead of continuing to buy natural gas which can change at the whim of the vagaries of the market. It can expand its territory and market without regulatory approval by offering solar power systems that free the home or office from the wires of the existing utility. It can provide leasing options for electric vehicles and hybrid vehicles and unite the transportation power system with the electric grid. It can begin now to provide distributed energy systems to homes, offices, neighborhoods, and entire developments. It can continue to provide the best demand side management and conservation programs for its customers.

It can provide time of day meters that allow Citizens to buy off-peak electricity at off-peak rates. It can maximize its return on its assets by seeking innovative partnerships with energy and communication companies.

In the future, Austin Energy will ultimately recharacterize itself. Not unlike the railroad companies, electric utilities will begin to redefine their mission. Is the electric utility in the business of providing electricity to run an air-conditioning unit or is it in the business of providing cool environments? Is the utility in the business of providing the electricity to run lights during the night or is it in the business of providing light? Should the utility provide fuel cells and solar systems to its customers? Should the utility expand into the transportation sector and provide electric or hybrid hydrogen cars through various purchasing and lease options?

All of these possibilities with the basic pledge of the utility to provide the best service at the best price with products that are reliable and innovative can be part of the operating ethic of Austin Energy now. It can do these things and make substantial-contributions to the general fund of the City thus providing other services for its Citizens.

SUSTAINABILITY

It is the hope and the purpose of this Community of the Future effort that Austin Energy lead and direct this city into the future with this vision of a great city. That we, as Austin Citizens, will choose to make decisions which not only provide for the citizens who are alive now, but also for those that will be alive in twenty years or fifty years. One definition or measure of sustainability is the ability to provide for the needs of the present Citizenry without prejudicing the rights, resource base, or environment of the future Citizenry. Sustainability was defined by the United Nations Brundtland Commission in 1987 as "meeting the needs of the present without compromising the ability of future generations to meet their own needs."

Intergenerational equity cannot be met by markets which do not set aside resources for the future or provide for the accounting of depleted natural resources. Markets, by their nature, reward the buyers that are in the market in real time. Free markets will cause the cheapest, easiest to find resources to be consumed first. Markets allocate resources based on those who are prepared to pay now. Sustainable Policies come from a deep understanding of the responsibility of the present generation to the generations that follow.

The Plan of this initiative is dedicated to the creation of a great city utility that has a deep understanding of this issue and this principle and to the well-being of the future Citizens of this City.

"Men make history, and not the other way around.
In periods where there is no leadership, society stands still.
Progress occurs when courageous, skillful leaders
seize the opportunity to change things for the better."

Harry S. Truman

Chapter One

Haste *makes* Waste

Our Declining Fuel Base

THE CONVENTIONAL VIEW

The 2002 <u>World Energy Outlook</u> of the International Energy Agency states in the Executive Summary:

"The world has abundant reserves of energy. Proven energy reserves are adequate to meet demand until 2020 and well beyond. Oil will be available throughout the period, although unconventional oil is likely to play a growing role. Proven reserves of natural gas and coal are abundant. There will be no lack of uranium for nuclear power production in the foreseeable future. Renewable Energy sources are plentiful and will be more widely used. Beyond 2020, new technologies, such as hydrogen based fuel cells and carbon sequestration, hold out the prospect of plentiful, clean energy supplies in a carbon-constrained world."

Indeed, according to the <u>Energy Information Agency</u>, world oil reserves are somewhere around a trillion barrels, and world gas reserves are around 5 thousand trillion cu. ft. Presently, the U.S. uses about 20 million barrels of oil a day and the world consumes around 75 million barrels a day. That's 7 billion a year for the U.S and over 27 billion for the world. Divide 27 billion into a trillion and you've got just less oil time left than Moses spent wandering around in the desert.

The numbers for natural gas are just as good. The U.S. consumes just less than 22 trillion cu. ft. a year and the world consumes just over 80 tcf. With 5 thousand trillion cu. ft. of reserves, we have maybe 60 years left. (1 1/2 Moses Wanderings). The US Geological Survey estimates that the United States has sufficient reserves for 45 years at current levels and 34 years at future demand levels. Whether it's 35 or 45 or 60 years, it's not very long. It's the time it takes to have children, watch them go to college for too long, and then have children of their own that grow up and then want to go to college for too long too. I used to think that 60 years was a long time. Now my friends who are 60 are still young. Paul McCartney just turned 60. Will we still need him in 4 more years?

Check the Energy Information Agency web page at http://www.eia.doe.gov/ or the site at British Petroleum http://www.bp.com/worldenergy/. On the EIA site, check out Table 15 under oil and gas supply. You will find out all you need to know about the production and consumption of energy.

The conventional view as expressed by Dr. Mark Mazur, Acting Administrator of the EIA before the Senate Energy and Natural Resources Committee on Dec 12, 2000 is this: "Available natural gas resources in the United States combined with supplies from foreign sources are believed to be adequate to meet demand increases expected through 2020."

PROBLEMS WITH RESERVE NUMBERS

One problem with the data is that it is political. For one reason or another, nations and companies choose not to represent their reserves actually. Some companies may underestimate their reserves for strategic reasons. Some nations may overestimate to receive larger quotas if quotas are based on reserves. Some companies may overestimate to make the balance statement look better. Others may underestimate to avoid potential tax liability.

Certainly, the United States is not interested in publishing on its official energy web site that it does not know where the energy to meet its future needs will come from or how those needs will be met. The EIA page looks exactly like it should.

This leads to the creation of technical reserves. Technical Reserves are often confidential. According to Jean Laherrere in his Sept 28, 2001 presentation to OPEC in their Vienna meeting, there is a huge difference between political values of reserves and technical values of reserves which are generally confidential for most countries. Yet, most production forecasts by official agencies are based on the political data.

"Unscientific reserve claims for political reasons may obscure the fact that most large, economic oil fields have been found, and permanent oil shock is inevitable early in the next century."

from WORLD OIL, October 1995

Usually reserves are classified on the degree of certainty. There is P for proven. 2P is proven plus probable, and 3P includes possible. In the U.S., the practice of only reporting proved reserves to comply with SEC rules means that the declared reserves are systematically under-reported, leaving room for future growth. Indeed, over the last 20 years, 88% of the annual additions of oil reserves come from the re-evaluation of past discoveries because the previous estimates were systematically too conservative.

These are the two major problems with reserve estimates. They are biased for political reasons and they are biased because of tax or regulatory reasons.

When you integrate these problems into reserve modeling, a different picture emerges.

THE CONTRARIANS

The most famous oil and gas geologist of the age is M. King Hubbert. In 1956, he predicted that oil production would peak in the lower 48 states in 1970. He was derided. Oil in the lower 48 peaked in 1970. His bell shaped curve is famous in the industry. The curve is justified as a statistical aggregation of many independent producing fields, but it does not work when exploration is discontinuous because of changing tax policies or price environments. The main mistake is to assume only one peak. However, Hubbert himself spoke to this:

> "The production rate begins at zero, increases exponentially during the early period of development, and then slows down, passes through one or more principal maxima, and finally declines negative exponentially to zero. There is no necessity that the curve P as a function of t, have a single maximum or that it be symmetrical. In fact, the smaller the region, the more irregular in shape is the curve likely to be. On the other hand, for large areas such as the United States or the world, the annual production curve results from the superposition of the production from thousands of separate fields. In such cases, the irregularities of small areas tend to cancel one another and the composite curve becomes a smooth curve with only a single practical maximum. However, there is no theoretical necessity that this curve be symmetrical. Whether it is or is not will have to be determined by the data themselves."

M. King Hubbert

There is a strong likelihood that the word "maxima" in the above quote is the equivalent of a brain speed bump and that "P as a function of t" is a red light that makes the eye and the brain find greener pasture. Nevertheless, the mind and thoughtfulness of Hubbert deserves comprehension. It is the basis of those who have come to a rather startling conclusion. This handful of Hubbert Curve apostles and high paid consultants believe that the peak of world oil production is going to occur in the middle of this decade. They believe that world gas production will peak in around 2020.

Perhaps the best exposition of the position is found in a paper published in <u>Scientific American</u> and found at the web site <u>http://www.dieoff.org/page140.htm</u>. Another good report is at <u>http://www.oilcrisis.com/de/lecture.html</u>. There is also an oil and gas expert in Houston by the name of

Matthew Simmons who is also making similar noises. His website speeches can be found at http://www.simmonscointl.com

And there are many others.

There is the straightforward prediction of Dr. Albert Barnett, a professor from The University of Colorado known for his unique ability to communicate the urgencies of population growth:

"MY ANALYSIS, BASED ON GEOLOGICAL ESTIMATES OF THE TOTAL WORLD RESOURCE OF PETROLEUM, SUGGESTS THAT WORLD PETROLEUM PRODUCTION WILL PEAK AROUND THE YEAR 2004 AND THEREAFTER WILL START ITS INEVITABLE DECLINE TOWARD ZERO."

In 1995, a respected consulting firm in the oil business called Petroconsultants published a report for oil industry insiders titled WORLD OIL SUPPLY 1930-2050 ($32,000 per copy) which concluded that world oil production could peak as soon as the year 2000 and decline to half that level by 2025. In the report, large and permanent increases in oil prices were predicted after the year 2000. The report says:

"No initiative put in place starting today can have a substantial effect on the peak production year. No Caspian Sea exploration, no drilling in the South China Sea, no SUV replacements, no renewable energy projects can be brought on at a sufficient rate to avoid a bidding war for the remaining oil."

There are others in the oil business who feel the same. One is Kenneth Deffeyes who recently wrote the book Hubbert's Curve:

"The petroleum era is coming to a close. Fossil fuels are a one-time gift that lifted us up from subsistence agriculture and eventually should lead us to a future based on renewable resources," Deffeyes writes. Those are strong words for a man raised in the oil patch. For the rest of us, the end of the world's dependence on oil means we need to make some tough political and economic choices.

Another leading oil and gas expert who is actually an investment banker who claims to not be an expert is <u>Matthew Simmons</u> from Houston. Simmons writes:

"The U.S. is also the first country to experience a major depletion surprise. This occurred in 1970 or 1971 when we finally peaked as the world's leading oil producer; just as M. King Hubbert predicted we would. Once the U.S. reached its peak production rate (which occurred before the advent of Alaskan or deepwater oil) we produced over 9.5 million barrels per day. Years later, this same region's production had fallen to just under 7 million barrels per day, despite a quadrupling in oil well completions. Today, this region's oil production has fallen to only 3.5 million barrels per day. When production peaks, the declines follow regardless of how intensively one drills additional wells.

" I fear that 5 to 10 years from now, historians might look back and discover that natural gas in 2002 finally experienced the same fate as U.S. oil did 32 years earlier."

Another reserve contrarian is <u>Richard Nehring</u>:

"An energy crisis is descending over the world. The situation is grave. The world has not run out of oil and North America has not run out of natural gas. What we are short of is any way to grow our energy supply. North America has no excess natural gas capacity. What we do have is extremely aggressive decline rates, making it harder each year to keep current production from falling. A massive number of gas-fired power plants have been ordered. But the gas to run them is simply not there.

"The attraction of this vision is easy to understand. Natural gas has long been recognized as the cleanest fossil fuel. Moreover, natural gas-powered generating equipment is now highly thermally efficient, has a relatively low capital cost, and is easy to permit and install. When these substantial advantages are coupled with the promise of plentiful supplies of natural gas at reasonable prices, the combination seems almost too good to be true.

"This vision is indeed too good to be true"

Richard Nehring

Hubbert himself became concerned about the apparent lack of concern for depletion writing late in his life:

"Our window of opportunity is slowly closing...at the same time, it probably requires a spiral of adversity. In other words, things have to get worse before they can get better. The most important thing is to get a clear picture of the situation we're in, and the outlook for the future—exhaustion of oil and gas, that kind of thing...and an appraisal of where we are and what the time scale is. And the time scale is not centuries, it's decades."

One of Hubert's colleagues, LF Ivanhoe, published a paper in 1995 in World Oil. Since then, he has continued to publish his work regarding the decline of world oil reserves:

"It is concluded that the critical date per USGS data when global oil demand will exceed the world's production will fall somewhere between 2000-2010, and may occur very suddenly due to unpredictable political events. This is within the lifetimes of most people now alive. This foreseeable energy crisis will affect everyone on earth."

Perhaps the most vocal and controversial of the Contrarians is Dr. Colin J Campbell. In his presentation on oil reserves and the ramifications of that potential he concludes:

Peak oil is a turning point for Mankind
· 100 years of easy growth ends
· Population peaks too for not unrelated reasons
· The transition to decline is a period of great tension
· Priorities shift to self-sufficiency and sustainability
· It may end up a better world

And every now and then, you read something from Wall Street like this:

"The rig count over the last 12 years has reached bottom. This is not because of low oil price. The oil companies are not going to keep rigs employed to drill dry holes. They know it but are unable and willing to admit it. The great merger mania is nothing more than a scaling down of a dying industry in recognition that 90% of global conventional oil has already been found."

Goldman Sachs, August 1999

Daniel Yergen, the Pulitzer Award winning author of the much-publicized book on the oil industry, The Prize, says it well:

"In hindsight, the 1990s were the Big Bonfire, an unprecedented energy binge. As natural gas and gasoline prices shrunk, new houses and cars grew gargantuan. Soccer moms bought SUVs and Americans consumed their body weight in natural gas and oil every five days. Happy Hour is now over, and we are nursing a wicked hangover. The road ahead is strewn with energy potholes and related economic hazards.

"Whatever the twist and turns in global politics, whatever the ebb of imperial power and the flow of national pride, one trend in the decades following World War II progressed in a straight and rapidly ascending line — the consumption of oil. If it can be said, in the abstract, that the sun energized the planet, it was oil that now powered its human population, both in its familiar forms as fuel and in the proliferation of new petrochemical products. Oil emerged triumphant, the undisputed King, a monarch garbed in a dazzling array of plastics. He was generous to his loyal subjects, sharing his wealth to, and even beyond, the point of waste. His reign was a time of confidence, of growth, of expansion, of astonishing economic performance. His largesse transformed his kingdom, ushering in a new drive-in civilization. It was the Age of Hydrocarbon Man."

The Age of Hydrocarbon Man has truly been an age of cheap priced energy. Consider the following from the economist Walter Youngquist:

"Based on constant 1967 dollars, exclusive of taxes, the retail price of gasoline in the U.S. in 1920 was 49 cents, in 1930 it was 39 cents, in 1950 it was 37 cents, in 1970 it was 30 cents, and in 1974 it was 40 cents. The price in 1995 was 67.7 cents a gallon. But this 1995 price is for a much-improved quality of gasoline with additives for better engine performance, and also for reduction of air pollutants. The price is also for unleaded gasoline which was not available in 1974, and which costs more to produce than does leaded gasoline. This record of price stability is in marked contrast to the large increase in prices of virtually all other consumer items. The oil companies have done a remarkable job in supplying the world's largest consumer of gasoline, the U.S. citizen, with inexpensive high-quality gasoline without restrictions as to quantity."

The end of cheap energy leads many such as Joseph Tainter to the belief that a crash is imminent and that a reconsideration of our way of thinking is appropriate:

"Energy has always been the basis of cultural complexity and it always will be. ... the past clarifies potential paths to the future. One often-discussed path is cultural and economic simplicity and lower energy costs. This could come about through the "crash" that many fear — a genuine collapse over a period of one or two generations, with much violence, starvation, and loss of population. The alternative is the "soft landing" that many people hope for - a voluntary change to solar energy and green fuels, energy-conserving technologies, and less overall consumption. This is a utopian alternative that, as suggested above, will come about only if severe, prolonged hardship in industrial nations makes it attractive, and if economic growth and consumerism can be removed from the realm of ideology."

Yet, even with so many believing that we should begin to act boldly now to transition from the present carbon based economy to a solar hydrogen economy, there are the views of Nobel Laureates Paul Samuelson and William Nordhaus which state quite a different position:

"Should we be taking steps to limit the use of these most precious stocks of society's capital so that they will still be available for our grandchildren? ... Economists ask, Would future generations benefit more from larger stocks of natural capital such as oil, gas, and coal or from more produced capital such as additional scientists, better laboratories, and libraries linked together by information superhighways? ... in the long run, oil and gas are not essential."

Let us hope that this is true.

"Our ignorance is not as vast as our failure to use what we know"

M. King Hubbert

THE FUEL OF THE FUTURE

Most of the growth associated with proved reserves of oil and gas in the United States comes from higher estimates of recovery from existing fields, not from new discoveries. In fact, from 1977 through 1995, approximately 88 percent of the additions to U.S. proved reserves of crude oil and 74 percent of the additions to U.S. proved reserves of dry natural gas were due to this phenomenon, known as "reserves growth," or more accurately, "ultimate recovery appreciation (URA)."

Proved reserves of crude oil or natural gas are the estimated quantities that geological and engineering data demonstrate with reasonable certainty to be recoverable in the future from known reservoirs under existing economic and operating conditions at a particular time. Proved reserves estimates tend to be conservative, especially during the early years of a field's productive life when little is known about it. Estimates of ultimate recovery (current proved reserves plus production to date) tend to increase over time, driven primarily by improved geotechnical information, development of production technologies, and economic factors.

Despite knowledge of the drivers of URA, resource analysts have been handicapped by a lack of detailed serial data on estimated ultimate recovery and have had little success in accurately forecasting URA. As a result, reliable estimations of the size of the ultimate domestic inventory of oil and gas are unavailable, which is a critical impediment to energy-related decision-making by industry, individuals, and government. EIA and the U.S. Geological Survey are collaborating to develop a better understanding of processes that drive URA using EIA's recently developed Oil and Gas Integrated Field File (OGIFF), which provides annual estimated ultimate recovery data for more than 90 percent of the Nation's proved reserves from 1977 through 1995. (Office of Oil and Gas US DOE)

But if we are to believe Laherrere, there is a huge difference between political values of reserves and technical values of reserves, which are generally confidential for most countries. Yet most production forecasts by official agencies are based on the political data. Some countries report minimum values, some report maximum values. When technical data are used to calculate mean values of field reserves, a good fit is found between annual and cumulative discoveries and annual and cumulative production, the former being close to the latter with a time translation of a certain number of years. This procedure makes it possible to forecast future production from the corresponding past discovery trend. A long term forecast for World Production of all hydrocarbons, based on these methods, is far below all the scenarios developed for the 2000 Third Assessment report of the IPCC.

Laherrere concludes, "Most public reserve data are biased by politics, and are unreliable. They lead to false conclusions, be they the optimistic view that there is no need to be concerned by a possible scarcity of oil and natural gas, or the pessimistic view supporting extreme "green" attitudes, according to which, the world is heading to a catastrophe in terms of climate change. The data described in this paper, indicate that the oil production, outside OPEC Middle-East, would have started to decline in 1997 but for the arrival of deepwater oil and its fast rising production. Excluding deepwater, non Middle-East crude oil production has been level at around 46 Mb/day since 1988, apart from a bump in 1997 to 46.8 Mb/day, and will now start to decline. This overall decline is bound to continue and accelerate. So the uncertainty is the extent to which deepwater production, as well as that from the tar sands and extra-heavy oil can compensate for the decline of the non Middle-East production.

"These approaches need to be discussed and investigated in depth by the world community. It is necessary to establish a politically neutral agency (or institute) to gather true "mean" data on the world's reserves and productions."

Laherrere continues, "Consumers need to understand the prime importance of energy for life, and the need to avoid disruptions, oil producers have to realize that the best way to secure an overall agreement on the fair price is to tell the truth about their reserves. The developed and developing countries have to work together to determine what the reserves are and to find out if the future production is as ominous as the shifted discoveries curves suggest. They also need a better understanding of the price setting mechanisms, based on the cost of competing energies and on the impact of taxes in consuming countries. Finally, they all need to maintain a fair and stable oil price of the benefit (sic) not only to the producers and consumers of today, but also for our children and grandchildren. Everyone has to come to understand the true implications of past discovery and production trends, which demonstrate that the age of cheap oil has come to an end."

Because of issues of National Security, it is no surprise to find that the web page of the Energy Information Agency forecasts continued supplies of oil and natural gas, continued growth of consumption, and continued prices that are economically palatable. But the data seem to indicate something else. As a civilization, we have consumed about one trillion barrels of oil in the last 100 years or so. There are approximately that many barrels of oil left. Most of them are in the Middle East. More than 2/3rds of all known reserves are in Islamic countries. The Hubbert curve would suggest that we are indeed within a few years of peak oil production, depending on how OPEC chooses to influence the curve.

According to the <u>World Resources Institute</u>, total world energy supply is met by oil with 40%, coal with 26%, and natural gas with 24%. The rest is nuclear and renewable. In the US, coal provides 52% of our electricity, nuclear provides about 20%, natural gas is about 16%, hydropower provides around 7% and renewables are about 2%. Most oil is used to propel the transportation sector. In the US, we consume about 20 million barrels a day. We produce about 6. The fuel of choice in most new electrical generation plants is natural gas. We produce about 18 trillion cubic feet of natural gas per year. We consume over 24.

In the US, we produce about 75 Quadrillion BTUs of energy and consume about 100. The world consumes about 400. On the transportation side, we import more oil than we produce. That means that somewhere around 55% of our oil is now imported. The leading countries of origin of these imports are Saudi Arabia, Mexico, Venezuela, Canada, and Nigeria. The leading country of origin for natural gas is Canada.

The Energy Information Agency shows that reserves of natural gas will grow over the next 20 years from 156 trillion cu. ft. to approximately 175 trillion cu. ft. At consumption rates of 22 trillion per year, that is a 7-year reserve. For demand to grow and reserves to grow each year, more than 25 trillion cu ft. of gas must be added to reserves annually.

To avoid large imports from other countries, production must be increased above current levels. According to Leherrere, discovery in the early eighties from the US, Canada, and Mexico has dropped to less than 10 trillion cu. ft. per year. Shifting this discovery record by 20 years indicates that natural gas production from the US will be substantially less than the 25 trillion cubic feet needed to grow these reserves. These reserves will therefore be increased (if they are indeed increased?) not by discovery but by the process of reevaluation or reserve growth. As the Office of Oil and Gas of the Department of Energy has indicated, this process is difficult to predict and quantify. Therefore, it can be inferred from these data that the possibility of large imports of natural gas will be required to meet the needs of the United States.

TEXAS NATURAL GAS

Where will the natural gas for Texas power plants originate?

In Texas, we now consume more energy than we produce. We produce just over 6 trillion cubic feet of natural gas annually. We produce about 1.2 million barrels of oil a day. Texas' production is about 1/3 of the nation's gas and about 1/5 of our oil. In 1993, when energy policy groups analyzed the State's energy production and consumption, there was great disbelief that the State was on the verge of becoming a net energy importer. It has been like that for almost a decade.

Texas still has a surplus of natural gas production of about 2 trillion cu. ft. annually. Production is beginning to decline now after a strong decade of production in the 90s. However, the US as a whole is now importing about 4 trillion cu.ft. The amount of imported liquefied natural gas, the kind that can be placed in ships and does not need a pipeline, has tripled in the last 3 years. Where will this gas originate? Russia has the largest reserves with 1705 trillion cu. ft. The entire Mid-East has about the same. Closer to the US, Venezuela has about the same as the US with Argentina coming in a far distant second. In Africa, Algeria and Nigeria have the largest reserves of natural gas with about 150 tcf each.

A standard 500 MW combined cycle power plant running at a high capacity factor with a heat rate of 7500 BTUs/KWh can be expected to use 25 billion cu. ft. a year of natural gas. Over its 40-year life, it would use a trillion cu. ft. Twenty such new plants will consume 20 tcf.

The National Energy Policy Report states that the US annual natural gas use will increase from 22 tcf in 2000 to 35 tcf in 2020. To quote the report, "The most significant long-term challenge relating to natural gas is whether adequate supplies can be provided to meet sharply increased demand at reasonable prices."

The NEPR continues, "If supplies are not adequate, the high natural gas prices experienced over the past year could become a continuing problem, with consequent impacts on electricity prices, home heating bills, and the cost of industrial production." Given the data, it is hard to imagine that even regional supplies will be adequate. The solution will come in imported liquefied natural gas which will have increased transportation costs. As indicated above, there has been substantial growth in liquefied natural gas imports and a marked increase in the building of ship infrastructure in the last few years.

The World Energy Outlook published by the International Energy Agency states in its Executive Summary:

"The principal uncertainty in global energy supply prospects is cost. Advances in technology and productivity are driving production and transportation costs lower, but the depletion of the cheapest reserves and growing distances over which new supplies must be transported are, in many case, pushing delivered energy costs up. The net effect on supply costs varies among fuels and regions. The cost of supplying natural gas to the main markets is starting to rise with the depletion of near-to-market reserves and the growing need to ship gas from further afield. On the other hand, renewable energy sources, usually exploited at a local or regional level, are generally becoming less costly to produce.

"The other key factor in the energy-supply picture is the price. Energy prices play a major role in determining the timing and the amount of investment that goes into expanding energy supply capacity. Current supply, in turn, influences price. Because the oil market is partially cartelized, prices are well above the marginal cost of oil supply. Since gas competes with oil products, the oil price, as well as monopolistic elements in many gas markets, keeps the price of gas above its marginal costs too. Future oil prices are very uncertain since they depend heavily on the pricing and production policies of the major producing countries.

"Trade is poised to grow rapidly as a result of the regional mismatch between the location of demand and production. Dependence on the Middle East will continue to grow in the net oil-consuming regions, essentially the three OECD regions and some parts of Asia. This situation will increase mutual dependence, but can also be expected to intensify concerns about the world's vulnerability to a price shock induced by a supply disruption. Oil-supply chains will lengthen, and maintaining the security of international sea-lanes will become more important.

"Increasing dependence on imports of natural gas in Europe, North America and other regions will heighten those concerns (security concerns). On the other hand, the expected expansion of international LNG trade could alleviate the supply risks associated with long-distance rigid supply chains (pipelines) if it spurs more short term LNG trading and more flexible supply.

"Exploiting the world's gas resources will require massive investment in production facilities and infrastructure to transport gas to market. The share of transportation in total supply costs will rise, as supply chains lengthen with the depletion of reserves located closest to markets. Pipelines will remain the principal means of transport for gas, but liquefied natural gas is likely to play a growing role."

The Executive Summary continues:

"Developing renewable energy resources will require sustained investment in infrastructure. In the OECD, investment in renewables to achieve a 4% share in electricity generation in 2020 is expected to be $90 billion. This is equivalent to 10% of the total power sector investments over the next twenty years. If very strong efforts are made by governments to promote and subsidize renewables, their share could rise to 9% in 2020. The necessary investment requirements would be about 230 billion.

"Beyond 2020, the role of renewable energy in global energy supply is likely to become much more important."

And finally, the Outlook states:

"A number of technologies under consideration or active could radically alter the long-term supply picture. The main focus of current research on new supply technologies is hydrogen production and use. Hydrogen technology holds out the prospect of large-scale energy supply with minimal environmental impact.

"Hydrogen production may be based on the electrolysis of water using nuclear or renewable energy."

The fuel of the future is not natural gas-it is hydrogen. It seems to be the position of the OECD and EIA that in our haste to move forward into the future, we must waste the fuel of the present. The generations that follow us will likely question that position.

So should we.

Chapter Two

Some *are* Weatherwise, Some *are* Otherwise

Climate Change *and the* Environment

*"New opinions are always suspected,
and usually opposed, without any other reason
but because they are not already common."*

John Locke

CLIMATE CHANGE

In a recent Editorial, The Dallas Morning News offers the following in response to news of the present administration's policy and position on Climate Change:

"Now, in a new report to the United Nations, his (Bush) administration comes around to accepting the scientific consensus that global warming is real and that man is the culprit. It accepts the likelihood that economic and environmental disaster will occur — for example, that barrier islands (like those off the Texas coast) could disappear, that tropical diseases could spread and that the glaciers and snows that feed rivers could melt away.

But having appropriately changed its opinion about global warming, the administration shortsightedly fails to change its policy prescription. It continues to endorse a domestic policy alternative to Kyoto that would allow the United States to increase its emissions rather than decrease them. Furthermore, in a particularly disconcerting part of the report, it suggests that Americans simply will have to get used to global warming's negative effects.

It is good that the administration accepts the reality of global warming. Now it needs to bring its policy in line with that acceptance. Doing little or nothing is both bad policy and bad politics. Inaction may please coal mining executives, but it could cost Mr. Bush the support of another core constituency — suburban parents — who might think he is compromising their children's futures.

Polls show that Americans support action. A 2001 CBS News/New York Times poll showed that 72 percent of them think that it is necessary to take immediate steps to counter global warming. And a January poll by the Mellman Group showed that 71 percent of them support solving the country's energy problems by conserving energy through energy-efficiency measures and by developing alternative sources of energy.

Conservatives like Rush Limbaugh are wrong in saying that taking aggressive action to reduce greenhouse gas admissions is against conservative values. True conservatives are good stewards of the resources around them. True conservatives invest prudently now to avoid larger costs later. President Richard Nixon created the Environmental Protection Agency, and the first President George Bush signed the first anti-global warming treaty in 1992.

Rather than harming the economy, action could stimulate jobs in new areas. A 2000 study by the Tellus Institute of Massachusetts showed that Texas could create 84,000 jobs, increase wages by $3 billion and grow the state's economy by $2 billion by heavily investing in clean, renewable energy.

The administration should reconsider its global warming strategy. The level of the threat — to the environment and to Mr. Bush's political fortunes if he alienates voters who worry about their children's legacy — demands it."

"Men willingly believe what they wish."

Gaius Julius Caesar

THE SCIENCE OF CLIMATE CHANGE

The science of Climate Change may be assailable by its opponents, and in all fairness, there are serious holes in the International Panel on Climate Change (IPCC) and the World Meteorological Organization's (WMO) projections and models. These international organizations were charged by the UN in 1988 to assess the scientific and technical literature on climate change, predict the potential impacts of changes in climate, and evaluate options for the adaptation to and mitigation of climate change. Even with these holes, the data grows more and more impressive. Take this account out of William K. Steven's book, The Change in the Weather:

"On the 360-mile drive down the Richardson Highway from Fairbanks in the interior to Valdez on the coast, the meaning of the phrase "purple mountain majesty" becomes as clear as it ever is. In the right light, tall, jagged peaks of the Alaska Range project a soft lilac hue. But as one approaches the spectacular Chugach Range on the southern leg of the trip, the color shifts subtly in the lower elevations. The landscape still has a purplish look, but the purple has a gray cast to it. Whole mountainsides look dead, and in fact are; the white spruce that once adorned them have been killed en masse.

"Once these purple-gray stretches of tree skeletons were a green and vital part of the spruce-larch-aspen tapestry that makes up the taiga, the great boreal forest that circles the globe's northern reaches. Today, in a stretch of 300 or 400 miles reaching westward from the Richardson Highway, north of Valdez, past Anchorage, and down through the Kenai Peninsula, armies of spruce bark beetles are destroying the spruce canopy or have already done so. Often the trees are red instead of gray-freshly killed but not yet desiccated.

"These are the most magnificent, most valuable trees in Alaska: tall, reaching 100 feet, most sought after by loggers, the cream of the crop economically and the signature tree of the taiga. The beetles are "basically eliminating the canopy," Jerry Boughton, the Anchorage-based head of the U.S. Forest Service's regional forest health program, said in mid-1998. In the previous five years, he said, the beetles' assault on the spruce "just took off exponentially; it's an incredible phenomenon." Statistics are somewhat approximate, but they suggest that perhaps a third to a half of Alaska's white spruce have died in the last fifteen years.

"Glenn P. Juday, a forest ecologist at the University of Alaska in Fairbanks, is one of several who believes the warming climate is fundamentally responsible for the decline of the taiga. This would make sense, since the boreal forest by definition flourishes in colder temperatures. But Juday has identified a number of specific factors that in this view have combined to put the forest under extreme stress.

"One of them, strangely enough, is heavier snow. One day in mid 1998, Juday took a visitor to the Bonanza Creek Experimental Forest, a long-term ecological research reservation a few miles southwest of Fairbanks. At Bonanza Creek, not far from the Arctic Circle, white spruce trunks towered overhead, adorned by short, needled branches draped with delicate, wispy lichens. Juday pointed to the tops of two of the trees-they were missing, the crowns snapped off by the weight of snow. Normally, said Juday, snows in Alaska's interior have been light fluffy. But with a warmer climate and more moisture in the air, they have become heavier. Two especially heavy snowfalls in the late 1980s and early 1990s broke off the tops of the trees. After that, the damaged trees became easy prey for insects.

"That is not all. The warming climate, while bringing more snow to Alaska's interior in the winter, has also, perversely, made it drier in the summer. Warmth and lack of moisture, say Juday, have stunted the trees' growth. Not far away from Bonanza Creek, he pointed to a subtle but telling sign: The crowns of aspens looked thin and sparse, with small leaves. Crowns are where the most recent growth would have taken place. Finally, he said, the warming climate has stimulated outbreaks of tree-eating insects in general.

"Most damaging of all has been the spruce-bark beetle outbreak. "It has moved into high gear in the last six or seven years," said Juday. "It's just rolling through the forest." Jerry Boughton takes a somewhat cautious view of the role of climate in the outbreak, noting that a number of factors have combined to cause it. For one thing, the forest is more susceptible to insect attack because it is older. "But certainly," he said, "the warming has created a better environment for the bark beetle to expand."

"All in all, said Juday, the constellation of stresses promoted by the changing climate has put the taiga in real trouble: "We've got a sick forest here."

"Whether the taiga will migrate northward, as forests have in response to climate change in millennia past, remains to be seen. Some migration is expected, but there is not really all that much space between what is now the taiga's northern limit and the Arctic Ocean. Normally, forest types more tolerant of a warmer climate would move in behind the retreating taiga. But in Alaska's case, south of the state there is only ocean. Where would trees come from? And if they don't come, what would Alaska's future look like?

"The answers to those questions are far from clear."

The warming in the north is of a magnitude that few have seen. On average, summer days are about 11% warmer than they were thirty years ago. Three decades ago, the temperature in Fairbanks would reach 80 degrees for a total of about a week a summer. Now it does so for three weeks. The growing season is about 20% longer. But it doesn't rain as much, and crops are often parched.

The heavier snows of winter and greater heat of summer have combined to cause Alaska's permafrost-perpetually frozen ground- to thaw. As it thaws, pockets of ice trapped in the soil melt. This makes the land sink. The holes, called thermokarst, make drunken forest as trees shift in the sinking ground. The roads are lined by utility poles tilting at crazy angles. Houses are thrown off kilter. It's like a very slow earthquake.

As the boundary of the permafrost moves northward, it may disappear from Alaska completely. This may be good. And the longer summer does allow for more tourists to come see the sites. But then there is the problem of sites like Columbia Glacier, a three mile wide, thirty four mile long river of ice that flows imperceptibly into Prince William Sound. It has receded eight miles since 1983. Tourists can no longer see its majesty.

Glaciers all over the world have receded. In Greenland, according to a 1999 NASA study, the southern sheet had shrunk between 1993 and 1998 by 2 cubic miles of ice each year. The International Panel on Climate Change (IPCC) estimates that over the last century, the melted water from all these glaciers has contributed as much as 2 inches to the observed sea rise.

And who can forget the pictures of the North Pole two years ago showing it to be an ocean instead of the snowy home of Santa Claus.

"Men stumble over the truth from time to time, but most pick themselves up and hurry off as if nothing happened."

Winston Churchill

What does the Intergovernmental Panel on Climate Change (IPCC) say about the effects of Climate Change on North America? The following is edited from their most recent report. This is the best, most peer-reviewed science available on the subject.

Foreword

The Intergovernmental Panel on Climate Change (IPCC) was jointly established by the World Meteorological Organization and the United Nations Environment Programme in 1988 to assess the scientific and technical literature on climate change, the potential impacts of changes in climate, and options for adaptation to and mitigation of climate change. Since its inception, the IPCC has produced a series of Assessment Reports, Special Reports, Technical Papers, methodologies, and other products which have become standard works of reference, widely used by policymakers, scientists, and other experts.

This Special Report, which has been produced by Working Group II of the IPCC, builds on the Working Group's contribution to the Second Assessment Report (SAR), and incorporates more recent information made available since mid-1995. It has been prepared in response to a request from the Subsidiary Body for Scientific and Technological Advice (SBSTA) of the UN Framework Convention on Climate Change (UNFCCC). It addresses an important question posed by the Conference of the Parties (COP) to the UNFCCC, namely, the degree to which human conditions and the natural environment are vulnerable to the potential effects of climate change. The report establishes a common base of information regarding the potential costs and benefits of climatic change, including the evaluation of uncertainties, to help the COP (Conference of Parties) determine what adaptation and mitigation measures might be justified.

Executive Summary

Within the North American region (defined for the purposes of this report as the portion of continental North America south of the Arctic Circle and north of the U.S.-Mexico border), vulnerability to climate change varies significantly from sector to sector and from subregion to subregion. Recognition of this variability or subregional "texture" is important in understanding the potential effects of climate change on North America and in formulating viable response strategies.

The characteristics of the subregions and sectors of North America suggest that neither the impacts of climate change nor the response options will be uniform. This assessment suggests that there will be differences in the impacts of climate change across the region and within particular sectors. In fact, simply considering the relative climate sensitivity of different sectors or systems within a particular subregion (i.e., climate-sensitive, climate-insensitive, or climate-limited) would suggest differentiated impacts. This diversity also is reflected in the available response options. Sectors and subregions will need to adopt response options to alleviate negative impacts or take advantage of opportunities that not only address the impacts but are tailored to the needs and characteristics of that subregion.

Comprising most of Canada and the contiguous United States, this large area is diverse in terms of its geological, ecological, climatic, and socioeconomic structures. Temperature extremes range from well below -40°C in northern latitudes during the winter months to greater than +40°C in southern latitudes during the summer. The regional atmospheric circulation is governed mainly by upper-level westerly winds and subtropical weather systems, with tropical storms occasionally impacting on the Gulf of Mexico and Atlantic coasts during summer and autumn. The Great Plains (including the Canadian Prairies) and southeastern U.S. experience more severe weather—in the form of thunderstorms, tornadoes, and hail—than any other region of the world.

Our current understanding of the potential impacts of climate change is limited by critical uncertainties. One important uncertainty relates to the inadequacy of regional-scale climate projections relative to the spatial scales of variability in North American natural and human systems. This uncertainty is compounded further by the uncertainties inherent in ecological, economic, and social models—which thereby further limit our ability to identify the full extent of impacts or prescriptive adaptation measures. Given these uncertainties, particularly the inability to forecast futures, conclusions about regional impacts are not yet reliable and are limited to the sensitivity and vulnerability of physical, biological, and socioeconomic systems to climate change and climate variability.

Within most natural and human systems in North America, current climate—including its variability—frequently is a limiting factor. Climate, however, is only one of many factors that determine the overall condition of these systems. For example, projected population changes in North America and associated changes in land use and air and water quality will continue to put pressure on natural ecosystems (e.g., rangelands, wetlands, and coastal ecosystems). Projected changes in climate should be seen as an additional factor that can influence the health and existence of these ecosystems. In some cases, changes in climate will provide adaptive opportunities or could alleviate the pressure of multiple stresses; in other cases, climate change could hasten or broaden negative impacts, leading to reduced function or elimination of ecosystems.

Virtually all sectors within North America are vulnerable to climate change to some degree in some subregions. Although many sectors and regions are sensitive to climate change, the technological capability to adapt to climate change is readily available, for the most part. If appropriate adaptation strategies are identified and implemented in a timely fashion, the overall vulnerability of the region may be reduced. However, uncertainties exist about the feasibility of implementation and efficacy of technological adaptation.

Even when current adaptive capability has been factored in, long-lived natural forest ecosystems in the east and interior west; water resources in the southern plains; agriculture in the southeast and southern plains; human health in areas currently experiencing diminished urban air quality; northern ecosystems and habitats; estuarine beaches in developed areas; and low-latitude cold-water fisheries will remain among the most vulnerable sectors and regions. West coast coniferous forests; some western range-lands; energy costs for heating in the northern latitudes; salting and snow clearance costs; open-water season in northern channels and ports; and agriculture in the northern latitudes, the interior west, and west coast may benefit from opportunities associated with warmer temperatures or potentially from carbon dioxide (CO_2) fertilization.

The availability of better information on the potential impacts of climate change and the interaction of these impacts with other important factors that influence the health and productivity of natural and human systems is critical to providing the lead time necessary to take full advantage of opportunities for minimizing or adapting to impacts, as well as for allowing adequate opportunity for the development of the necessary institutional and financial capacity to manage change.

Key Impacts to Physical, Biological, and Socioeconomic Systems

Ecosystems: Nonforest Terrestrial (Section 8.3.1).The composition and geographic distribution of many ecosystems will shift as individual species respond to changes in climate. There will likely be reductions in biological diversity and in the goods and services that nonforest terrestrial ecosystems provide to society.

Increased temperatures could reduce sub-arctic (i.e., tundra and taiga/tundra) ecosystems. Loss of migratory wildfowl and mammal breeding and forage habitats may occur within the taiga/tundra, which is projected to nearly disappear from mainland areas. This ecozone currently is the home of the majority of the Inuit population. It also provides the major breeding and nesting grounds for a variety of migratory birds and the major summer range and calving grounds for Canada's largest caribou herd, as well as habitat for a number of ecologically significant plant and animal species critical to the subsistence lifestyles of the indigenous peoples. Current biogeographic model projections suggest that tundra and taiga/tundra ecosystems may be reduced by as much as two-thirds of their present size, reducing the regional storage of carbon in the higher latitudes of North America—which may shift the tundra region from a net sink to a net source of CO_2 for the tundra region.

The relatively certain northward shift of the southern boundary of permafrost areas (projected to be about 500 km by the middle of the 21st century) will impact ecosystems, infrastructure, and wildlife in the altered areas through terrain slumping, increased sediment loadings to rivers and lakes, and dramatically altered hydrology; affected peatlands could become sources rather than sinks for atmospheric carbon. Projections suggest that peatlands may disappear from south of 60°N in the Mackenzie

Basin; patchy arctic wetlands currently supported by surface flow also may not persist.

Elevated CO_2 concentrations may alter the nitrogen cycle, drought survival mechanisms (e.g., the rate of depletion of soil water by grasses), and fire frequency—potentially decreasing forage quality and impacting forage production on rangelands. Increases in CO_2 and changes in regional climate could exacerbate the existing problem of loss of production on western rangelands related to woody and noxious plant invasions by accelerating the invasion of woody C_3 plants (many crop and tree species) into mostly C_4 (tropical grasses, many weed species) grasslands. Mechanisms include changes in water-use efficiency (WUE), the nitrogen cycle (increase in carbon-to-nitrogen ratio and concentrations of unpalatable and toxic substances), drought survival mechanisms, and fire frequency. Growth and reproduction of individual animals could decrease as CO_2 concentrations rise, without dietary supplementation. However, the data are ambiguous, and production may increase in some grassland ecosystems. Uncertainty exists in our ability to predict ecosystem or individual species responses to elevated CO_2 and global warming at either the regional or global scale.

Arid lands may increase. Current biogeographical model simulations indicate up to a 200% increase in leaf area index in the desert southwest region of North America and a northern migration and expansion of arid-land species into the Great Basin region of North America. Although uncertainty exists in predictions of regional climate changes and simulations of ecosystem responses to elevated CO_2 and global warming, long-term change in ecosystem structure and function is suggested.

Landslides and debris flows in unstable Rocky Mountain areas and possibly elsewhere could become more common as winter wet precipitation increases, permafrost degrades, and/or glaciers retreat. Water quality would be affected by increased sediment loads. Fish and wildlife habitat, as well as roads and other artificial structures, could be at increased risk.

Ecosystems: Forested (Section 8.3.2). Changes are likely in the growth and regeneration capacity of forests in many subregions. In some cases, this process will alter the function and composition of forests significantly.

Forests may die or decline in density in some regions because of drought, pest infestations, and fire; in other regions, forests may increase in both area and density. Models suggest that total potential forest area could increase by as much as 25–44%. For some individual forest types, however, range expansions could be preceded by decline or dieback over 19–96% of their area while the climate and ecosystems are adjusting, but before an equilibrium is attained. Even though total forest area could increase, northward shifts in distribution could produce losses in forest area in the United States.

Geographic ranges of forest ecosystems are expected to shift northward and upward in altitude, but forests cannot move across the land surface as rapidly as climate is projected to change. The faster the rate of climate change, the greater the probability of ecosystem disruption and species extinction. Climate-induced dieback could begin within a few decades from the present and might be enhanced by increases in pest infestations and fire. Alternatively, forest growth might increase in the early stages of global warming, followed by drought-induced forest dieback after higher temperatures have significantly increased evaporative demand. Migration into colder areas may be limited by seed dispersal (e.g., barriers may exist because of urbanization and changing land-use patterns), seedling establishment, and poor soils. As forests expand or contract in response to climate change, they will likely either replace or be replaced by savannas, shrublands, or grasslands. Imbalances between rates of expansion and contraction could result in a large pulse of carbon to the atmosphere during the transition.

Longer fire seasons and potentially more frequent and larger fires are likely. Because of decades of fire suppression—resulting in higher forest densities and increased transpiration—forests in the continental interior are experiencing increased drought stress; pest infestations; and catastrophic, stand-replacing fires, potentially resulting in changes in species composition. Future climate could result in longer fire seasons and potentially more frequent and larger fires in all forest zones (even those that currently do not support much fire), due to more severe fire weather, changes in fire management practices, and possible forest decline or dieback.

Hydrology and Water Resources (Section 8.3.3). Water is a linchpin that integrates many subregions and sectors. Water quantity and quality will be directly affected by climate change. Available water supplies also will be affected by changes in demand from multiple sectors competing for water resources. Changes in the hydrological cycle will cause changes in ecosystems—which will, in turn, affect human health (e.g., by altering the geographic distribution of infectious diseases) and biological diversity.

Increases or decreases in annual runoff could occur over much of the lower latitudes and in midcontinental regions of mid and high latitudes. Increases in temperature lead to a rise in evapotranspiration—which, unless offset by large increases in precipitation or decreases in plant water use, results in declines in runoff, lake levels, and groundwater recharge and levels. The greatest impact of declines in supply will be in arid and semi-arid regions and in areas with a high ratio of use relative to available renewable supply, as well as in basins with multiple competing uses. Alternatively, regions that experience substantial increases in precipitation are likely to have substantial increases in runoff and river flows.

Climate projections suggest increased runoff in winter and early spring but reduced flows during summer in regions in which hydrology is dominated by snowmelt. Glaciers are expected to retreat, and their contributions to summer flows will decline as peak flows shift to winter or early spring. In mountainous regions, particularly at mid-elevations, warming leads to a long-term reduction in peak snow-water equivalent; the snowpack builds later and melts sooner. Snow- or glacier-fed river and reservoir systems that supply spring and summer flow during the critical periods of high agricultural and municipal demand and low precipitation may tend to release their water earlier in the year, which would reduce supplies during summer droughts. Water supplies and water quality, irrigation, hydroelectric generation, tourism, and fish habitat, as well as the viability of the livestock industry, may be negatively impacted. The Great Plains of the United States and prairie regions of Canada and California are particularly vulnerable.

Altered precipitation and temperature regimes may cause lower lake levels, especially in midcontinental regions and, along with the seasonal pattern and variability of water levels of wetlands, thereby affect their functioning—including flood protection, water filtration, carbon storage, and waterfowl/ wildlife habitat. The response of an affected wetland varies; it might include migration along river edges or the slope of a receding lake and/or altered vegetation species composition. Long-term lake levels would decline to or below historic low levels in the Great Lakes under several climate change scenarios. Prairie pothole lakes and sloughs may dry out more frequently in the north-central regions of North America. These wetlands currently yield 50–75% of all waterfowl produced annually in North America. In the Mackenzie delta of arctic Canada, many lakes could disappear in several decades because of decreased flood frequency and less precipitation.

Increases in hydrological variability (larger floods and longer droughts) are likely to result in increased sediment loading and erosion, degraded shorelines, reductions in water quality, reduced water supply for dilution of point-source water pollutants and assimilation of waste heat loads, and reduced stability of aquatic ecosystems. Projected changes in snowfall and snowmelt—as well as suggested increases in warm-period rainfall intensity—could shift the periodicity of the flood regime in North America, possibly stressing the adequacy of dams, culverts, levees, storm drains, and other flood prevention infrastructures.

The impacts of flooding are likely to be largest in arid regions, where riparian vegetation is sparse; in agricultural areas during winter, when soils are more exposed; and in urban areas with more impervious surfaces. Increases in hydrological variability may reduce productivity and biodiversity in streams and rivers and have large impacts on water resources management in North America, with increased expenditures for flood management. Increases in water temperature and reduced flows in streams and rivers may result in lower dissolved oxygen concentrations, particularly in summer low-flow periods in low- and mid-latitude areas.

Projected increases in human demand for water would exacerbate problems associated with the management of water supply and quality. Managing increased water demands will be particularly problematic in regions experiencing increases in variability and declines in runoff. Improved management of water infrastructure, pricing policies, and demand-side management of supply have the potential to mitigate some of the impacts of increasing water demand.

Food and Fiber: Agriculture (Section 8.3.4). As the climate warms, crop patterns will shift northward. Most studies of these shifts have focused on changes in average climate and assume farmers effectively adapt. They have not fully accounted for changes in climate variability, water availability, and imperfect responses by farmers to changing climate. Future consideration of these factors could either increase or decrease the magnitude of changes projected by these earlier studies.

Climate modifications that lead to changes in daily and interannual variability in temperatures and, in particular, precipitation will impact crop yields. Although changes in average temperature and precipitation can be expected to impact agriculture, few studies have considered the effects of increased climate variability on crop and livestock production. Increased variability in daily and interannual temperature and precipitation are likely to be as important or more important than the effects of mean changes in climate. Droughts, floods, and increased risks of winter injury will contribute to a greater frequency and severity of crop failure. An increased reliance on precision farming has increased vulnerability to climate variability outside a narrow range of change. These impacts are projected to be both site- and crop-specific; reliable forecasts for such occurrences, however, are not yet regionally available.

The direct effects of a doubling of CO_2 on crop yields are largely beneficial. Food and fiber production for crops like cotton soybean, and wheat are expected to increase an average of 30% (range -10% to +80%) in response to a doubling of CO_2 concentration. The magnitude of this response will be highly variable and will depend on the availability of plant nutrients, temperature, and precipitation.

Crop losses due to weeds, insects, and diseases are likely to increase and may provide additional challenges for agricultural sector adaptation to climate change. Less severe winters due to climate change may increase the range and severity of insect and disease infestations. Increasing pressure to reduce chemical inputs (i.e., pesticides) in agriculture will necessitate a greater emphasis on concepts of integrated pest management and targeted application of agricultural chemicals through precision agricultural technologies.

Recent analyses of issues of long-run sustainability associated with agricultural adaptation to climate change from an arbitrary doubling of equivalent CO_2 concentrations have concluded that there is considerably more sectoral flexibility and adaptation potential than was found in earlier analyses. Much of this reassessment arises from a realization that the costs and benefits of climate change cannot be adequately evaluated independently of behavioral, economic, and institutional adjustments required by changing climate. Although scientific controversy over the nature and rate of climate change remains, most existing scenarios suggest gradual changes in mean climate over decades—providing ample opportunities for adaptation measures to be implemented within vulnerable subregions of North America. However, uncertainties remain about the implications of changes in climate variability, as well as crop responses to increases beyond a doubling of equivalent atmospheric CO_2 concentrations.

Existing studies that have looked at changes in mean temperature and precipitation suggest that climate change is not likely to harm agriculture enough to significantly affect the overall economy of North America. The economic consequences of climate change to U.S. agriculture are expected to be both positive and negative, depending on the nature of temperature and precipitation changes that occur in specific subregions. Subregions of North America that are dependent on agriculture may be more vulnerable than areas offering economic diversity. The Great Plains area, for example, relies heavily on crop and livestock production and, as a result, is potentially vulnerable to climate change, with negative consequences projected for southern extremes and potential positive impacts in northern areas as temperatures rise. Warmer temperatures at northern latitudes may lessen the adverse effects of frost damage, but the risk of early- and late-season frost will remain a barrier to the introduction of new crops.

Consumers and producers could gain or lose; the long-term stability of the forest-products market is uncertain. Consumer prices could increase by 100–250% with severe forest dieback, producing losses of 4–20% of the net value of commercial forests. Alternatively, consumer prices could decrease with increased forest growth and harvest in Canada, and producers could sustain economic losses. With exports from Canada to the United States, however, the net changes (consumers plus producers) could be negative for Canadians and positive for the U.S. market.

Food and Fiber: Production Forestry (Section 8.3.5). The most intensively managed industry and private forestlands may be least at risk of long-term decline from the impacts of climate change because the relatively high value of these resources is likely to encourage adaptive management strategies. Private forest managers have the financial incentive and the flexibility to protect against extensive loss from climate-related impacts. They can use several available techniques: short rotations to reduce the length of time that a tree is influenced by unfavorable climate conditions; planting of improved varieties developed through selection, breeding, or genetic engineering to reduce vulnerability; and thinning, weeding, managing pests, irrigating, improving drainage, and fertilizing to improve general vigor. Such actions would reduce the probability of moisture stress and secondary risks from fire, insects, and disease. However, the more rapid the rate of climate change, the more it may strain the ability to create infrastructure for seeding or planting of trees, or to support the supply of timber if there is a large amount of salvage. A fast rate of warming also may limit species constrained by slow dispersal rates and/or habitat fragmentation, or those that are already stressed by other factors, such as pollution.

Food and Fiber: Fisheries and Aquatic Systems (Section 8.3.6). Aquatic ecosystem functions will be affected by climate change, although the effects are likely to vary in magnitude and direction depending on the region.

Projected increases in water temperature, changes in freshwater flows and mixing regimes, and changes in water quality could result in changes in the survival, reproductive capacity, and growth of freshwater fish and salmonid and other anadromous species. In larger, deeper lakes—including the Great Lakes and many high-latitude lakes—increases in water temperature may increase the survival and growth of most fish species. In smaller, mid-latitude lakes and streams, however, increased water temperatures may reduce available habitat for some cold-water and cool-water species. Increased production rates of food (e.g., plankton) with warmer water temperature (e.g., plankton production increases by a factor of 2–4 with each 10°C increase) also may increase fish productivity. However, shifts in species composition of prey with warming may prevent or reduce productivity gains if preferred prey species are eliminated or reduced. Warmer freshwater temperatures and changes in the pattern of flows in spawning streams/rivers could reduce the abundance of salmon, although individual size may increase from improved growth in the warmer water. Increases in temperature in freshwater rearing areas and increased winter flows may increase mortality for stocks in southern rivers on the west coast.

Freshwater species distributions could shift northward, with widespread/subregional species extinction likely at the lower latitudes and expansion at the higher latitudes of species ranges. For example, a 3.8°C increase in mean annual air temperature is projected to eliminate more than 50% of the habitat of brook trout in the southern Appalachian mountains, whereas a similar temperature increase could expand the ranges of smallmouth bass and yellow perch northward across Canada by about 500 km. Whether fish are able to move or will become extinct in response to changes in or loss of habitat will depend on the availability of migration routes.

Recreational fishing is a highly valued activity that could incur losses in some regions resulting from climate-induced changes in fisheries. The net economic effect of changes in recreational fishing opportunities is dependent on whether the gains in cool- and warm-water fish habitat offset the losses in cold-water fish habitat. The loss of fishing opportunities could be severe in some parts of the region, especially at the southern boundaries of fish species' habitat ranges. Although gains in cool- and warm-water fishing opportunities may offset losses in cold-water fishing opportunities, distributional effects will cause concern.

There will likely be relatively small economic and food supply consequences at the regional/national level as a result of the impacts on marine fisheries; however, impacts are expected to be more pronounced at the subregional and community levels. The adaptability of fisheries to current climate variability and the relatively short time horizons on capital replacement (ships and plants) will minimize the regional- and national-level impacts of projected climate change. At the subregional and community levels, however, positive and negative impacts can be significant as a result of suggested shifts in the centers of production and ensuing relocation of support structures, processors, and people.

Projected changes in water temperatures, as well as salinity and currents, can affect the growth, survival, reproduction, and spatial distribution of marine fish species and the competitors and predators that influence the dynamics of these species. Growth rates, ages of sexual maturity, and distributions of some marine fish species are sensitive to water temperatures (e.g., cold temperatures typically result in delayed spawning, whereas warm temperatures result in earlier spawning), and long-term temperature changes can lead to expansion or contraction of the distribution ranges of some species. These changes generally are most evident near the northern or southern species boundaries (i.e., warming resulting in a distributional shift northward, and cooling drawing species southward).

The survival, health, migration, and distribution of many North American marine mammals and sea turtles are expected to be impacted by projected changes in the climate through impacts on their food supply, sea-ice extent, and breeding habitats. Although some flexibility exists in their need for specific habitats, some marine mammals and sea turtles may be more severely affected than others by projected changes in the availability of necessary habitat, including pupping and nesting beaches; in food supplies; and in associated prey species. Concerns are the result primarily of projected changes in seasonal sea-ice extent and accelerated succession or loss of coastal ecosystems as a result of projected rises in sea level.

Coastal Systems (Section 8.3.7). The implications of rising sea level are well understood, in part because sea level has been rising relative to the land along most of the coast of North America for thousands of years. Some coastal areas in the region will experience greater increases in sea level than others. Adaptation to rising seas is possible, but it comes at ecological, economic, and social costs.

In the next century, rising sea level could inundate approximately 50% of North American coastal wetlands and a significant portion of dry land areas that currently are less than 50 cm above sea level. In some areas, wetlands and estuarine beaches may be squeezed between advancing seas and engineering structures. A 50-cm rise in sea level would cause a net loss of 17–43% of U.S. coastal wetlands, even if no additional bulkheads or dikes are erected to prevent new wetland creation as formerly dry lands are inundated. Furthermore, in the United States, 8,500–19,000 km^2 of dry land are within 50 cm of high tide, 5,700–15,800 km^2 of which currently are undeveloped. Several states in the United States have enacted regulations to adapt to climate change by prohibiting structures that block the landward migration of wetlands and beaches. The mid-Atlantic, south Atlantic, and Gulf coasts are likely to lose large areas of wetlands if sea-level rise accelerates.

Coastal areas in the Arctic and extreme North Atlantic and Pacific are less vulnerable, except where sea ice and/or permafrost currently is present at the shoreline. Recent modeling suggests that projected increases in ocean fetches as a result of decreases in the period and extent of sea-ice cover could increase wave heights by 16–40% and therefore increase coastal erosion during the open-water season. Maximum coastal erosion rates are expected to continue in those areas where permafrost contains considerable pore, wedge, or massive ice or where the permafrost shoreline is exposed to the sea.

Rising sea level is likely to increase flooding of low-lying coastal areas and associated human settlements and infrastructure. Higher sea levels would provide a higher base for storm surges; a 1-m rise would enable a 15-year storm to flood many areas that today are flooded only by a 100-year storm. Sea-level rises of 30 cm and 90 cm would increase the size of the 100-year floodplain in the United States from its 1990 estimate of 50,500 km^2 to 59,500 km^2 and 69,900 km^2, respectively. Assuming that current development trends continue, flood damages incurred by a representative property subject to sea-level rise are projected to increase by 36–58% for a 30-cm rise and by 102–200% for a 90-cm rise. In Canada, Charlottetown, Prince Edward Island appears to be especially vulnerable, with some of the highest-valued property in the downtown core and significant parts of the sewage systems at risk.

Saltwater is likely to intrude further inland and upstream. Higher sea level enables saltwater to penetrate farther upstream in rivers and estuaries. In low-lying areas such as river deltas, saltwater intrusion could contaminate drinking water and reduce the productivity of agricultural lands.

Human Settlements and Industry (Section 8.3.8). Climate change and resulting sea-level rise can have a number of direct effects on human settlements, as well as effects experienced indirectly through impacts on other sectors.

Potential changes in climate could have positive and negative impacts on the operation and maintenance costs of North American land and water transportation systems. Higher temperatures are expected to result in lower maintenance costs for northern transportation systems, especially with fewer freeze-thaw cycles and less snow. However, some increased pavement buckling is a possibility because of projected longer periods of intense heat. Problems associated with permafrost thawing in the Bering Sea region could be particularly severe and costly. River and lake transportation could be somewhat more difficult, with increases in periods of disruption as a result of projected decreases in water levels (e.g., the Mississippi River and the Great Lakes-St. Lawrence Seaway system). Increases in the length of the ice-free season could have positive impacts for commercial shipping on the inland waterways and in northern ports (e.g., Arctic Ocean ports).

Projected changes in climate could increase risks to property and human health/life as a result of changes in exposure to natural hazards (e.g., wildfire, landslides, and extreme weather events). A large and increasing number of people and their property in North America are vulnerable to natural hazards. Projected changes in wildfires and landslides could increase property losses and increase disruptions and damages to urban and industrial infrastructure (e.g., road and rail transportation and pipeline systems). Although some questions remain regarding the extent and regional reflections of changes in extreme weather events as a result of climate changes, projected changes in the frequency or intensity of these events are of concern because of the implications for social and economic costs in a number of sectors. For example, extreme weather events can cause direct physical harm to humans; disrupt health infrastructure, causing contamination of water systems and creating breeding sites for insects or favorable conditions for rodents that carry diseases; and affect construction costs, insurance fees and settlement costs, and offshore oil and gas exploration and extraction costs.

Climate warming could result in increased demand for cooling energy and decreased demand for heating energy, with the overall net effect varying among geographic regions. Changes in energy demand for comfort, however, are expected to result in a net saving overall for North America. Projected increases in temperature could reduce energy use associated with space heating [e.g., a 1°C increase in temperature could reduce U.S. space-heating energy use by 11% of demand, resulting in a cost saving of $5.5 billion (1991$US)]. It also has been projected that a 4°C warming could decrease site energy use for commercial-sector heating and cooling by 13–17% and associated primary energy by 2–7%, depending on the degree to which advanced building designs penetrate the market. If peak demand for electricity occurs in the winter, maximum demand is likely to fall as a result of projected temperature changes, whereas if there is a summer peak, maximum demand will rise.

The technological capacity to adapt to climate change is likely to be readily available in North America, but its application will be realized only if the necessary information is available (sufficiently far in advance in relation to the planning horizons and lifetimes of investments) and the institutional and financial capacity to manage change exists. Some adaptations can be made without explicit climate predictions through increasing the resilience of systems, such as greater flood control, larger water reservoirs, and so forth, but these approaches are not without social and economic costs. Rapid changes in climate and associated acceleration of sea-level rise would limit adaptation options, thereby putting considerable strain on social and economic systems and increasing the need for explicit adaptation strategies.

Human Health (Section 8.3.9). Climate can have wide-ranging and potentially adverse effects on human health through direct pathways (e.g., thermal stress and extreme weather/climate events) and indirect pathways (e.g., disease vectors and infectious agents, environmental and occupational exposures to toxic substances, and food production).

Direct health effects include increased heat-related mortality and illness and the beneficial effects of milder winters on cold-related mortality. Under a warmer North America, current models indicate that by the middle of the next century, many major cities could experience as many as several hundred to thousands of extra heat-related deaths annually. The elderly, persons with preexisting health conditions, and the very young (0—4 years) are most vulnerable to heat stress. Gradual acclimatization to increasing temperatures, the use of air conditioners, and an adequate warning system for heat waves may help reduce heat-related deaths. Conversely, it has been suggested that winter mortality rates may decrease in the future with warmer winter temperatures.

Climate warming may exacerbate respiratory disorders associated with reduced air quality and affects the seasonality of certain allergic respiratory disorders. Concurrent hot weather and exposure to air pollutants can have synergistic impacts on health. Recent studies show a positive correlation between ground-level ozone and respiratory-related hospital admissions in the United States and Canada. Increased temperatures under climate change could lead to a greater number of days on which ozone levels exceed air quality standards. Global warming also may alter the production of plant aero-allergens, intensifying the severity of seasonal allergies.

Changing climate conditions may lead to the northward spread of vector-borne infectious diseases and potentially enhanced transmission dynamics due to warmer ambient temperatures. Vector-borne infectious diseases (e.g., malaria, dengue fever, encephalitis) and waterborne diarrheal diseases currently cause a large proportion of global fatalities. Temperature increases under climate change are expected to enlarge the potential transmission zones of these vectors into temperate regions of North America. Some increases in waterborne diseases may occur due to changes in water distribution, temperature, and microorganism proliferation under climate change. However, the North American health infrastructure likely would prevent a large increase in the actual number of vector-borne and waterborne disease cases.

"Nothing makes a man, or a body of men, as mad as the truth. If there is no truth in it, they laugh it off."

Will Rogers

THE REALITY OF THE FUTURE

Predicting the effects of Climate Change in and around the City of Austin is more than difficult. As the IPCC report says, "conclusions about regional impacts are not yet reliable and are limited to the sensitivity and vulnerability of physical, biological, and socioeconomic systems to climate change and climate variability."

But consider these possibilities.

We may see changes in the amount of water in the Colorado River. That will affect our water supply. We may see less rain and when it comes, it will come in larger events making floods more likely. The ground will be dryer because of the increased evaporation. Water tables may drop. Trees may die. New trees may move into replace them or new ones may need to be introduced. Imagine an Austin with the tree canopy of Laredo.

If we have less rain, then our yards will need more watering. Saint Augustine grass may become unaffordable. Xeriscaping would likely be more commonplace.

Our electric bills will go up in the summer unless we make our homes and the equipment in them more efficient. Going outdoors in the summer afternoon may become just a memory of the old ones. Barton Springs may become a legend in memory only.

There will be more bugs. Your roof will not last as long. (unless it is white) The roads will buckle more from the heat, but they may not freeze as much. You may have to paint your house more often. Your car will fade both inside and outside faster. The seats inside will burn you for real if you don't put a sun visor on the dash or get a solar powered ventilator.

On the positive side, winters will get milder and milder and they are already pretty nice. You may not have to bring in your plants at all. Your heating bill should go down. You will hear more Mexican Doves cooing as they migrate north. It seems like there are more Crows too. Your pets will probably not freeze in the winter but they may need to have their hair cut shorter and more often in the summer. There will be other bonuses with climate change- like longer growing seasons and the potential of increased plant growth from the heavier concentration of CO_2. Many of them may end up providing significant positive economic impact.

AIR QUALITY

Like any other large city whose transportation base is the car, Air quality in Austin gets worse each year. Almost every morning after the rush hour, our city finds itself enshrouded in a cloud of dirty particulates and smog. Austin, like Dallas and most of the other Metro areas in Texas, currently has periods of air quality that do not meet Environmental Protection Agency standards. When bad air occurs over and over, the EPA designates the area as a non-attainment area. Dallas is a non-attainment area as is Houston. Austin is characterized as near nonattainment. We are familiar with "Ozone Action Days." We are advised to not fill up the car with gas, or to use a gas lawn mower on these days. We are urged to ride the bus for free! But these techniques are mostly palliative. They are designed to postpone an almost certain non-attainment designation from being applied to the local airshed.

But ozone is not just an invention of EPA scientists or some bothersome regulatory issue that must be gamed; it is a real health hazard at ground level.

Ozone is an intensely irritating gas. At levels routinely found in the air in many American cities during summer months, ozone can damage the lungs and airways, causing them to become inflamed, reddened and swollen. This response can cause coughing, burning sensations and shortness of breath.

Research on the effects of prolonged exposure to relatively low levels of ozone has found reductions in lung function, inflammation of the lung lining and breathing discomfort. In studies of animals, ozone exposure has been found to increase susceptibility to bacterial pneumonia infection. One study of 16 Canadian cities over a 10-year period found that air pollution, including ozone, at relatively low concentrations, is associated with excess admissions to the hospital for respiratory diseases.

Ozone levels generally rise during the May through September period when higher temperatures and the increased amount of sunlight combine with the stagnant atmospheric conditions that are associated with ozone air pollution episodes.

Recently, scientists have begun to focus on the effects of long-term, repeated exposure to high levels of ozone. A study of college freshmen who were lifelong residents of California found a strong relationship between lifetime ozone exposure and reduced lung function.[2] Additional evidence comes from a study of 72 cadets at the U.S. Military Academy at West Point, who attended a summer training program in which they spent an average of 11 hours a day outdoors. The study found that the 21 cadets who attended summer training in Fort Dix, New Jersey, an area with elevated ozone levels, had a larger drop in lung function over the summer, compared with the cadets who trained at sites in Georgia, Missouri and Oklahoma with lower ozone levels.[3]

High ozone levels are particularly dangerous for people with asthma. When ozone levels are high, more people with asthma suffer attacks that require a doctor's visit or use of extra medication.

State of the Air: 2002, a report by the American Lung Association, finds that ozone continues to be a very serious problem in the United States.

Three-quarters of the nation's population who reside in areas with ozone monitors—a total of 142,668,846 Americans—are breathing in unhealthy amounts of ozone pollution. The overall number of high-ozone days in unhealthy ranges dipped 3.5% from 2001 to 2002 in monitored counties, but the number jumped 18.5% between 2000 and 2002.

Of the 10.2 million American adults with asthma who live in counties with ozone monitors, 7.6 million—more than 70%—lived in counties that received an "F" rating in ozone pollution. Of the 2.6 million children living in counties with monitors who had an asthma attack last year, 1.9 million—more than 70%—live in counties receiving an "F" rating.

Of the almost 2 million Americans with emphysema living in those monitored counties, 1.5 million live in counties with an "F" rating in ozone pollution, while of the 6.3 million Americans with chronic bronchitis, 4.7 million live in "F"-rated counties.

Of the nation's over-65 population who live in these monitored counties, almost three quarters live in counties that received an "F" rating in ozone pollution.

It has been estimated that bad air kills or accelerates the deaths of 50,000 Americans every year. About that many Americans die each year in automobile accidents.

In Austin, although statistics are not available, it can be inferred from these morbidity rates that 250 Austinites will prematurely fall victim to bad air every year. Those Austinites who suffer from chronic allergies exacerbated by bad air dwarf that number.

"It wasn't raining when Noah built the ark."

Howard Ruff

THE FUTURE OF THE WEATHER

There is relatively little that the City of Austin can do to change the Change in the weather. True, we can characterize our actions as a very small piece of a very large pie towards climate stabilization. Even a major move to sustainable energy sources probably will not change the future we have already cast for ourselves. It will change the future for the generations that follow us though.

We can make our roofs white. We can cover them with solar panels. We can walk to work. We can telecommute. We can erect more and more wind fields and begin to commission state of the art solar parks to power our needs. We can make our homes and buildings super efficient. We can fill them with super efficient appliances and air conditioners. We can install reversible fuel cell stations in our neighborhoods. We can move boldly towards a hydrogen based sustainable energy local economy in our transportation and electric sectors.

But, the coming changes will not be deterred. The coming changes will not even be mitigated by the massive deployment of these technologies and strategies on a community scale.

These technologies and strategies will allow us to adapt to the change and they will reduce the costs of that adaptation. We may even be able to profit by becoming a commercial and industrial bastion of these technologies as the rest of the communities of the world struggle with the rigors of their own adaptation to the Change.

The massive deployment and use of these technologies and strategies will leave us with something we do have control over.

WE will have <u>CLEAN AIR.</u>

"We make our own fortunes and we call them fate."

Disraeli

Chapter Three

A Penny Saved *is a* Penny Earned

Green Buildings, Conservation, *and* Renewables

"It's pretty hard to be efficient without being obnoxious."

Ken Hubbard

EFFICIENCY

Perhaps it was Jimmy Carter who with all best intentions made conservation a bad thing. You may remember his speeches to the nation with his sweater on. He had lowered the thermostat in the White House and was asking that we all do the same. It was the beginning of the steepest rise in oil prices this nation had ever endured. We turned off the lights at Christmas. Our skyscraper skylines were no longer visible at night as signs of our prosperity. We were in the "Energy Crisis".

Many of the conservation programs present today found their genesis in the Carter years. Soon after Carter urged us to conserve, Ronald Reagan replaced him. Not long after that, the City of Austin initiated its first conservation efforts. Most conservation today is really efficiency. Real conservation programs would deal with the root of our consumption. Or they ask us to really do with less as President Carter did with the resetting of the White House thermostat. Conservation programs are as popular as cedar pollen.

Programs that introduce and stimulate the adoption of smarter devices and appliances are really efficiency programs. A light bulb that gives the same amount of lumens of light for 1/3 the power is smart. It is not a tacit confession that you cannot afford the light bulb that needs more power to do the same job; it is a straightforward act of intelligence. To reject a car that gets 8 miles per gallon (say a Bentley) for a Lexus that gets 30 miles per gallon is not an admission of an inability to pay, it is more a market based IQ test.

Who would walk to his car in the front drive by going out the back door day after day?

If it's not stupid, it certainly does not make much sense. And, some would argue that wasting finite resources is plain old wrong.

As Dwight Eisenhower said in his farewell address, "As we peer into society's future, we - you and I, and our government — must avoid the impulse to live only for today, plundering for our own ease and convenience, the precious resources of tomorrow."

Doing more with less makes our domestic industries more competitive, it makes our homes more affordable, and traveling for the simple enjoyment of traveling more likely. It allows resources and capital to be directed and invested into other pursuits and ventures. It makes the costs of living less. And, in a carbon-based economy, an efficient system makes for less pollution and more clean air and water.

The American economy has made substantial improvements in efficiency over the past 30 years. In 1973 it took 19,000 BTUs to produce one dollar of GNP. Today that ratio is closer to 11,000 BTUs to one dollar of GNP. Yet the nations of Western Europe and Japan are almost twice as efficient. This ratio is important. If energy costs 2 dollars per 100,000 BTUs (7 cents/KWh), then every dollar of GNP requires 22 cents of energy. It is a large constituent in the costs of the goods we, as a nation, sell to ourselves and others.

During the last 30 years, we have seen appliances improve greatly in their ability to produce more work with less energy. A refrigerator 30 years ago would use over 1700 KWhs a year. Today's new refrigerators use just over 500 KWhs a year. The newest air conditioning units with the highest EERs outperform their older generations by a ratio of 2 to 1. New clothes washers use half the energy and water of their predecessors. Occupancy sensors turn out lights in the bathroom no matter how many teenagers you have. Computer monitors go to sleep when no one is typing.

The Chevy Impala of 1970 might have averaged 12 miles to the gallon while my 2000 Chevy Impala averages well over 20. However, since 1990, the fuel efficiency improvements of the American light vehicle fleet have been flat. And when you consider the increased penetration of trucks and SUVs into the market, overall vehicle efficiency in 2000 is no better than the efficiency of the fleet 20 years ago. At the same time, Toyota and Honda and other international competitors are now building and marketing hybrids that are pushing 50 miles to the gallon.

CONSERVATION IN AUSTIN

The idea that conservation could save or defer the building of another power plant became a powerful idea in the early 1980s. It resulted in the creation of a conservation department dedicated to building a conservation power plant. Today, Austin Energy's conservation Energy Division provides residential energy efficiency and commercial energy management services to all types of residential and commercial customers of Austin Energy. These services include providing technical assistance through energy audits to identify energy efficiency opportunities, making recommendations on the most cost effective measures, while offering financial incentives for the installation of energy efficient measures.

The purpose of these programs is to maximize efficiency in the use of Austin's energy resources while increasing customer comfort and satisfaction. They also reduce customer's bills. Maximizing efficiency also reduces emissions, and it promotes economic development.

In 2001, it is estimated that the programs achieved a reduction in overall system demand of 45 megawatts in required power plant capacity. Total energy saved in 2001 from this increase in conservation is estimated to be over 54 thousand MWhs. The combined effect of all of Austin Energy's Conservation Programs will save over 600 GWhs this year. That means that the combined effect of Austin Energy's conservation efforts is equivalent to one large coal plant. And it has been avoided without the loss of convenience or comfort. Indeed, what has been avoided is the pollution, the loss of real estate to generation, and the depletion of a finite resource. One less coal plant is a significant accomplishment.

This year's increase in conservation represents 30 metric tons of sulfur dioxide, 72 metric tons of nitrous oxides, 27 metric tons of carbon monoxide, and 35,000 tons of carbon dioxide that will not be added to our atmosphere. Over 3 tons of particulates were avoided from falling on the windshields of the cars that seem to constantly need cleaning. The combined effect of all conservation programs would represent savings that are roughly 10 times these numbers.

These savings were achieved through savings in both the residential and commercial sectors. In the residential area there is the Appliance Efficiency Program, which provides rebates for high efficiency central AC units and window units. Under this program rebates are also available for solar hot water heaters and heat recovery hot water systems in all electric homes. The Total Home Efficiency Program allows customers to borrow money at low interest rates to pay for home improvements such as solar screens, attic insulation, sealing and repair of duct systems and even solar photovoltaic panels. The Total Home Efficiency program also has a rebate program that works best for customers who can arrange their own financing.

There is a free Weatherization Program for low income, elderly and disabled customers. There is a Multifamily Incentive Program for landlords. There is the Power Partner Program that gives participants a free Honeywell Programmable Thermostat for the right to cycle the AC unit during peak loads for brief periods. A similar program called the Cycle Saver Program will turn off the hot water heater during peak for a one-time 25 dollar credit.

Homeowners can also take advantage of the Duct Diagnostic and Sealing Program. This program provides residential customers advanced testing on their ducts. Current testing shows that the average duct leakage in the Austin area is 25% and average airflow is 79% of the rated capacity.

On the Commercial Energy Management side, Austin Energy provides On Site Energy Surveys, at no cost, to identify energy efficiency opportunities. There are Commercial Rebates for efficient lighting, HVAC, thermal cool storage, motors, energy management control systems, and other custom technologies. Related to this program is the Small Business Lighting Program which offers discounts for lighting purchases. There is also a Commercial Power Partner Program that allows Austin Energy to cycle the AC during peak times. On the larger side, through the Load Cooperative Program, customers with large loads of 200KW receive cash incentives for agreeing to turn off loads during high demand.

Similarly, there is the Thermal Energy Storage Program that strives to reduce peak demand by shifting load to off-peak periods. Through the District Cooling Plant program, Austin Energy can serve the needs of several buildings. A downtown system is currently under construction to provide heating and cooling for two hotels, the convention center, the new city hall and several other office buildings and apartments. During on-peak hours, the chillers are shut down and an ice thermal storage tank is discharged to provide cooling to the buildings.

On the institutional side, Austin Energy can provide customized energy consultations and energy project solutions to institutional and governmental agencies through Interlocal Agreements. Austin Energy rebates can be allocated for energy conservation projects, and project financing solutions can also be identified. Through a revolving loan fund, the Municipal Energy

Conservation Program provides direct technical assistance to City of Austin municipal departments to implement energy efficiency projects in City-owned buildings.

BUILDINGS

In XENOPHON'S MEMORABILIA, written 2400 years ago, Socrates observed:

"Now in houses with a south aspect, the sun's rays penetrate into the porticos in winter, but in the summer, the path of the sun is right over our heads and above the roof, so that there is shade. If then this is the best arrangement, we should build the south side loftier to get the winter sun and the north side lower to keep out the winter winds. To put it shortly, the house in which the owner can find a pleasant retreat at all seasons and can store his belongings safely is presumably at once the pleasantest and the most beautiful."

Twenty-five years ago, when the "Solar Age" was just beginning, there was this great debate in solar circles. There was this one group who thought that solar energy was this equipment that would go on top of your house and do something. It would heat your water mostly. This was not very sexy, but it was reasonably well understood. If you put enough of this equipment on top of your house, you could even heat your house if you lived somewhere where you needed heat bad enough to make such a big deal out of it.

You could even possibly cool your house with these panels. I did one of these. It wasn't a house; it was actually a commercial building.

Energy from the sun was intercepted in flat plate panels that faced south, and collected in the water that circulated in the grooves of the black metal embedded behind the double insulated glass. This hot water was used to power something called an absorption chiller, which unlike most ACs, worked on ammonia, not Freon. The absorption chiller worked on the same principle as the large systems that cool large universities and other large buildings. But this system was small by those standards. If the sunlight during the summer was insufficient, (and what is the chance of that?) we could back up the system with natural gas that could provide back up heat for the absorption chiller. We even installed a multi-fuel boiler that would allow the owner to burn wood crates. Wood crates to air-conditioning! We were definitely on the cutting edge.

The system worked too. At least it worked for a little while.

There were problems. Even in the summer, the panels would not heat the water enough to drive the absorption chiller efficiently. We basically had a rather inefficient gas AC system.

Then there was this other group. They maintained that Solar was not equipment on top of roofs, but rather they argued, rather eloquently, that the Solar Age would be more likely ushered in by a new breed of homes and buildings that were themselves solar collectors. They, like the structures referred to by Socrates, would be sensitive to the environment they were placed in. They would be cool in the summer and warm in the winter because they were smart, energy conscious structures with eaves that knew what the latitude was and windows that knew which direction was south and where the sun was in the late afternoon when it is 100 degrees outside. They would have windows that opened. They would have windows that might turn opaque to the sun when the building needed no more insolation. (The word of art for solar energy coming into a given space) They might be bermed into the ground on the north. They might even have a long buried earth air exchanger that conditioned the air that cooled the envelope of the house.

Such Passive Solar Energy structures became the saving grace of the Solar Age as it became clear that ugly hot water devices poking holes in perfectly good roofs would not a revolution make. And the proponents were architects. Who could ask for a better, more informed profession to represent the virtues and promise of the coming Age of Solar?

Two decades later, Passive Solar Architecture is still alive and perhaps even well. But it has turned into something else. That something else is "Green Building". Green Building has turned into a great deal more than just passive solar architecture even though it includes most of those techniques developed in the 70s. Green Buildings include water use, materials, energy, and recycling, as well as landscapes that are appropriate. These homes and structures are efficient. They use less electricity, less water, and they release less offensive and unhealthy gases into the living environment.

THE AUSTIN GREEN BUILDING PROGRAM

"Sustainable design is not a reworking of conventional approaches and technologies, but a fundamental change in thinking and ways of operating-you can't put spots on an elephant and call it a cheetah."

Carol Franklin, Andropogon Associates Ltd.

The Green Building Program was initiated in the City of Austin through a grant awarded in 1990 from the Urban Consortium Energy Task Force. The purpose of the grant was to develop a Sustainable Systems Rating Program. In partnership with the Center for Maximum Potential Building Systems, a compilation of technical and logistical information was developed. Since 1993, Austin Energy has funded the operation and staff assigned to the Program. The program received an international award from the United Nations at the Rio de Janeiro "Earth Summit" in 1992.

The purpose of the Program at its inception in 1990 was to develop a Sustainable Systems Rating Program that can be used as a marketing tool to encourage high levels of resource conservation, appropriate resource usage, and positive economic development in new residential homebuilding. Rating systems such as Austin's Energy Star Rating Program for new homes have become a recognized, effective method to bring about energy conservation. This "Sustainability Rating" included general guidelines and themes. They strive to optimize the use of site resources in a non-deleterious manner. Scoring is based on conserving all resources and on recycling and the use of recycled materials. Points are given for stimulating the regional economy. Other considerations include minimizing embodied energy and negative environmental impacts, and simulating natural processes. The minimization of health threats to building occupants, producers, and environment is also considered in the scoring. Recently, guidelines and scoring for community issues such as impact on existing infrastructure were added.

The final point rating, "the sustainability score," is reduced to the categories of One Star for good, Two Stars for very good, Three Stars for excellent, and Four Stars for superior. The One Star Rating was determined by measures, which go beyond standard practice, yet are readily available and not cost prohibitive. Ratings in the Two to Four Star categories are achieved by including options that, while not always costly or difficult, require more commitment from the builder and the homeowner. In 1998 the Green Building Program's residential group further expanded its focus by developing a similar rating system for multi-family projects.

In 1994, a City Council resolution directed the creation of Sustainable Building Guidelines with special attention to the building of the new Austin-Bergstrom International Airport. The Guidelines provide a framework for designing and building municipal structures in Austin that are potentially more functional and pleasurable than conventionally built buildings. The objective of these guidelines is to inform clients and other professionals that the City of Austin wants to encourage sustainable design, environmental measures, and buildings in general that surpass current energy and land development codes.

The new City Hall will be an example of this potential. It will have a solar photovoltaic awning, efficient lighting, and daylighting. Cooling will be provided by a district chilling plant. The design and construction will feature the most efficient systems currently available and integrated with each other so that each enhances the efficiency of all others.

To address private commercial development, the Commercial Green Building Program functions as the central clearinghouse for all City of Austin sustainability programs. Because Green Building Program staff become involved in projects at the programming stage of design they are able to direct the design team to other City resources that provide financial incentives or other resources. Thus, rather than awarding a rebate based on simply installing an improved HVAC system near the end of the project, the program ensures that all available resources have been used to maximum advantage and that all systems complement one another.

The fundamental strategy of the Austin Green Building Program is to inform buyers of the more "earth friendly" options available to them when building a new home or commercial building. Its goal is to educate building professionals and use the building industry as a mechanism for distributing information on sustainable building. The ultimate goal is to transform the marketplace.

In 2001, the Green Building Program contributed 44,000 MWhs to the Austin Energy mix of resources. This represents over 6 metric tons of sulfur dioxide and 6 tons of carbon monoxide, 16 tons of nitrogen oxides, and almost 8,000 tons of carbon dioxide that were not added to the atmosphere for the year.

ZERO ENERGY BUILDINGS (ZEBs)

"You see things, and you say "Why"; but dream things that never were, and I say "Why not?"

Bernard Shaw

There is no reason why buildings should need outside power. Except for the tallest multistory buildings, almost every building has enough surface area on its roof and south facing walls to convert incoming solar energy to sufficient electrical energy to power its heating, cooling, lighting, appliance, and communication needs.

The average house in Austin uses around 12,000 KWhs annually. This is about 33 KWhs a day. The average horizontal surface at this latitude will intercept enough solar energy to transform that energy via a photovoltaic transducer to about 60 watt/hrs per square foot per day. Five hundred and fifty square feet would provide about 33 KWhs a day.

Of course, not all homes have roofs that are well positioned to receive sunlight, and others may be extensively shaded by trees or even other buildings; but, most new developments can and should be planned to facilitate the maximum solar potential.

A zero net energy home generates more power than it uses at peak demand. During times of power outage, the home generates its own power or runs on its own energy storage thus providing the homeowner essential energy security. The potential was demonstrated by the Florida Solar Energy Center. At their demonstration project in Lakeland, two identical homes were built with the same floor plan on nearby lots. The control home conformed to local building practices and codes. The other was designed with a maximum concern for energy efficiency and the implementation of solar technology. Both homes were approximately 2400 square feet in size.

The control home was constructed like most homes built in Florida right now. It had a gray/brown asphalt shingle roof with 11/2 foot overhangs. The home had R-30 insulation in the ceiling and R-4 insulation on the interior face of the concrete block walls. (Standard for Florida) The windows were single-glazed aluminum frame windows. The air conditioner was a standard 4-ton SEER 10 heat pump with R-6 ducts in the attic. The electric range, electric hot water heater, refrigerator, and electric dryer were all standard. Lighting was provided by 30 incandescent recessed can light fixtures.

The Zero Energy home had a white tile roof with 3-foot overhangs. Attic insulation was the same as the control house with an R-30. However, R-10 insulation was placed on the outside of the concrete block system. The windows were advanced solar control double-glazed windows. The air-conditioner was downsized to a 2 ton SEER 15.0. It had a variable speed blower, oversized, interior-mounted ducts, and a programmable thermostat. A high efficiency refrigerator was installed along with high efficiency compact fluorescent lighting. On the solar side, a 2 KW hot water heater and a rather modest 4 KW utility interactive PV system were utilized.

The two homes were monitored for a year throughout the seasons. (If Florida still has seasons)

During the peak month of June, the control home used 1,839 KWhs to run just the AC. The Zero Energy home consumed 837 KWhs in June of 1998, but the 4 KW PV system produced 502 KWhs. Total net use of the ZEB home was 335 KWhs. Total net use of the control home was well over 2,000 KWhs. The 4-KW PV system took up only a small portion of the white tile roof. (400 square feet) Part of the array faced south, but another subsection faced west to provide maximum production during the later afternoon. At 5:00 p.m. on June 18th, the utility experienced its annual summer peak demand. In fact, it was the hottest daytime temperatures ever recorded in Lakeland. The Zero Energy home produced more energy than it consumed at 4:30 and 5:30. During the course of the day, the Zero Energy home consumed a remarkable 199 watt hours of utility supplied power. At 8 cents/KWh, that is about 1.5 cents.

Had the ZEB home been outfitted with another 100 watts of PV power, it would have been a net provider to the utility for the day and at peak. With another 900 watts, it would have provided approximately 20% of its demand back to the utility.

During this peak day, the ZEB over a 24 hour period used 72% less power for air-conditioning, and it maintained cooler indoor temperatures. According to the FSEC, 29% of these savings were delivered by the high efficiency AC, high performance windows delivered 19% of the savings, the white tile roof was responsible for 16%, and the oversized interior ducts produced 14 % of the savings. Duct tightness contributed another 8%. The 3-foot over-hangs provided 7%, while the R10 walls saved 4%, and overall house tightness saved 3%.

Zero Energy Buildings can also be more than just houses. In the south of London is a housing development with a difference. It is the most environmentally friendly development for housing and work in all of Great Britain. Here, the Peabody Trust together with BP Solar have built 82 properties for rent and sale plus 16,000 square meters of workspace. More than 110 photovoltaic modules have been integrated into the façade of the building and are now generating renewable electricity. The project will consume only 25% of the electricity of the standard housing project. In addition, its residents can buy electric cars at reduced prices.

RENEWABLE ENERGY

A KWh generated by Renewable Energy Now is a KWh saved for our Children.

The City of Austin electric utility started as a renewable utility. In 1895, the first dam across the Colorado was completed and renewable hydroelectricity flowed from the water that it tried to tame. It didn't tame the Colorado very long. But, the dam was rebuilt and it was rebuilt right.

Ninety years later, another renewable facility was dedicated. It was the 300 KW PV Power Plant at the Decker Generation Station. Today, through its purchases and many other installations, the Austin Energy mix of resources includes almost 100 Megawatts of renewable energy. Most of this comes from a wind facility on a great mesa in West Texas that overlooks the Pecos River. This mesa is now a shining beacon of the growing wind-power industry. Along its ridges, dozens of great turbines can be seen facing the strong winds with elegance and serene beauty. The blades, larger than the largest of any airliner, turn slowly and deliberately. Each turbine, taller than the largest office buildings in Downtown Austin, produces enough energy for hundreds of homes. Windpower has come of age and Austin Energy is part of that Age.

"One of the deepest functions of a living organism is to look ahead...to produce future."

Francois Jacob

In the last fifteen years, Austin Energy has led the nation in the deployment of renewable energy. There was the 3M Solar Power Plant and the Austin Youth Hostel Solar Power Plant in 1990. The next year, the ECHO Village Senior Housing Solar Power Plant, the Solar Powered Water Meter Systems Project, and the Barton Creek Greenbelt Hike and Bike Trail Solar Lighting projects were completed. The Austin Convention Center Solar Power Plant was completed in 1992 and the Town Lake Center Solar Power Plant was dedicated 1993. In 1995, Council authorized the first major purchase of power from the Texas Wind Power Project. From 1995 to 1999, there was the Mary Moore Searight Park Solar Lighting project, the power purchase from BFI's Sunset Farm Landfill Gas to Electric Project, the Center for Maximum Potential Building Systems Solar Power Plant, the Dillo Solar Explorer Project, the Howson Library Solar Explorer Project, the Airport Solar Explorer Project, and the Wild Basin Solar Rooftop. In 1999 alone, twelve 1.5 KW solar rooftop projects, and four 3.0 KW solar rooftop projects were completed.

In that year, Council resolved that 5% of Austin's electric generation capacity should come from Renewables by 2005. Austin Energy is on track to accomplish that goal on time.

The Austin Green Choice program began in 2000. To provide for this program, 360 million KWhs have been contracted for from wind and landfill gas and an additional 25MW of wind is now in the final stages of negotiation and approval. That will bring total renewable energy capacity to 111 MW. Total KWhs sold in the Program is currently 207,046,508 KWhs. Key Accounts buy 106,185,877 KWhs, Small commercial uses 20,832,631, and residential customers use approximately 80,028,000 KWhs of that total.

The Austin Energy Green Choice Program is rated highly nationally because it provides clean renewable energy to customers who want it at a price that is only nominally above the regular rate. Plus, it provides 10 years of fuel price escalation protection. Therefore, the decision to join the Program is not just a question of the right thing to do; it is also potentially the smart thing to do.

> **"The worst thing about the future is that it gets here faster than it used to."**

SUSTAINABILITY

In 1998, the Sustainable Energy Task Force for the City of Austin published its report "Choose Clean Energy". The purpose of the report was to provide a direction to "Establish Austin as a leader in Sustainable Energy" while at the same time, "develop a plan to meet Austin's sustainable energy goals while maintaining or enhancing the City's future financial condition."

In the Executive Summary, the report states, "For the transformation of the utility to commence, the City must first acknowledge that its current generation mix is non-sustainable." It continues, "Green Power can become an important tool in near term efforts to enhance the competitiveness of the electric utility... and offers a non-polluting approach to the City's commitment to reducing debt on its conventional fossil fuel and nuclear power resources."

Of the seven major recommendations in the Report, all have been acted upon to one degree or another. The final Recommendation, to Craft a Business Plan to Maximize Success, is the purpose and focus of the Community of the Future initiative.

The City of Austin Vision Statement states that, We want to be the most livable community in the country.

The Austin Energy Mission Statement states that, Austin Energy provides extraordinary customer service, affordable and reliable energy, environmental leadership and exceptional value for our community.

Over the long term, affordable and reliable energy will need to be sustainable.

Sustainability was defined by the United Nations Brundtland Commission is 1987 as "meeting the needs of the present without compromising the ability of future generations to meet their own needs."

Using the least expensive fuels now and leaving the most expensive fuels to our children is not sustainable.

Polluting the air to the point that Austin becomes susceptible to federal EPA ozone standard remedies is not environmental leadership.

"We cannot solve problems with the same thinking we had when we created the problems."

Albert Einstein

Chapter Four

Never Confuse Motion *with* Action

Transportation

"Failure to prepare is preparing to fail."

Benjamin Franklin

When I got up this morning, I went downstairs and got the fresh orange juice out of the refrigerator and poured maybe eight ounces out of the container into the glass that I use every morning. Then, I cut up a Washington Pink Lady apple and place it on a little plate. Almost simultaneously, I pour some Raisin Bran into the chipped Mexican bowl that sits in the drain board. I drink the orange juice, rinse the glass, eat the apple slices, and sprinkle pure cane sugar onto the crisp tops of the overpriced Whole Food Erewhon cereal. I add some milk, just a quick slosh of heavy cream, and then stand in front of my less than roaring fake gas fireplace and stare out the living room window while I mix the contents with my spoon thinking to myself what a glorious breakfast I am enjoying.

The orange juice came from Florida, the apple is from Washington, the grain in the cereal probably came from the Midwest, but it was milled and packaged in Massachusetts, and the raisins were grown who knows where. The sugar may have come from Sugarland, Texas, about 150 miles to the south, and the milk may have come from Brenham, Texas, the home of Blue Bell Ice Cream about 100 miles to the east. The milk was then shipped to Houston where it was packaged and then shipped backed to Central Texas. The gas that burns in my fake fireplace probably came from South Texas. The water I use to rinse out the glass comes from the Colorado River Basin from rain that may have fallen last year perhaps a hundred miles upstream.

All in all, my simple yet glorious meal may have involved the movement of these basic products by perhaps 5,000 miles. Much of this would have occurred on one of the great achievements of our lifetimes, the beginning and the completion of the Interstate Highway System. It wasn't always this way. In the beginning of the 20th century, the idea of traveling by car from Maine to California was basically unthinkable. Dwight D. Eisenhower took an army convoy across the country before World War II, and it took him weeks. It must have been one of those memories that stuck. As President, he would be the major force that pushed the Interstate System through the Congress.

After I finish my Interstate Highway breakfast, I start up my Chevy Impala and drive from 23rd Street to Barton Springs Road. This is a rather modest commute. Commute is not even the right word really. The biggest mystery used to be whether or not the parking garage will have spaces available. That mystery has receded now that the new parking garage across the street that looks like it has prison guard towers is finished. If there was an underground metro, I would take it no doubt. It there was a light rail running down Guadalupe, I would probably take it. There is a bus and I don't take it.

I do like to play like I am in some great city. (Perhaps I am.) I walk across the pedestrian part of the South First Bridge, which I like a lot. I often stop at the widened section and look at the scullers gracing the lake leaving those V's in their wake until they almost cover the surface. Then they disappear. I walk to the Italian restaurant on 4th and Congress and watch the lunch crowd. Austin feels like a real city during lunch on Congress on a beautiful spring day. Sometimes I splurge and eat on the outdoor patio of the Four Seasons and enjoy the sounds and light of the lake and the amazing amount of people who walk and bike its trails. It's not like Santa Monica, mind you, where there is a separate lane for walkers and another lane for bikers and roller bladers right next to it, but it is pretty encouraging.

I walk back to work after lunch knowing that I will be back on the Lake by sunset running with the hundreds of other joggers, walkers, strollers, bicyclists, and occasional fishers. (There are still signs that say don't eat the fish.) This for me is Austin at its very best. It is Central Park meets the Seine without the language barriers.

In a few days or weeks, the director of the <u>Clean Air Force</u> will be informed that tomorrow will be an Ozone Alert Day. He will notify the press. Those are the days that the Citizens of Austin are asked to not mow or trim their lawns, or fill their cars up with gas. We are urged to carpool. The buses are free. The local weatherman will report it as if it is a natural event.

I know of no one who pays the least bit of attention to an Ozone Action Day. It's probably mostly noted as a day with reduced income for Capital Metro. However, as most policy makers and decision makers know, ozone non-attainment is a dog with bite.

Ozone non-attainment means that federal highway funds will be withheld if something is not done to improve the quality of the air. And make no mistake about it. Bad air kills thousands of people every year, young and old. It shortens lives. It makes for a lower quality of living for tens of thousands who suffer from allergies. Even with increased nitrous oxide, bad air is no laughing matter.

I find it ironic that one of the most understood of Hollywood suicide techniques is starting the car in the garage and not opening the door. What I don't understand is why we think that opening the door makes it any safer. It certainly does delay the effect, but will the ultimate result be any different?

> *"We've got to pause and ask ourselves:*
> *How much clean air do we need?"*
>
> *Lee Iacocca*

Unhealthy air does come from Houston. It does come from construction machines that belch unburned and burned carbon like dinosaurs on a diet from the La Brea Tar Pit. It does come from those horrible noisy blowers that put dust in the air and push leaves and trash on your neighbors' property. But the truth is, about 1/3 of our total emissions comes from our cars, trucks, boats, and SUVs. Most of the rest come from our utilities. However, the emissions that cause the smog in our cities do come primarily from our mobile sources.

According to the American Automobile Manufacturers Association, there are just over a half a billion vehicles in the World. World Human Population is around 6 billion. That means the ratio of people to cars is 11.7 (Worldwatch). Here, in Austin, the ratio is lower. In fact, it is not just lower; there are more cars in Travis County than there are people. There are about a billion bicycles in the world. Sometimes I wonder if most of these are around the University.

Everyone that I know seems to think that Amsterdam is a great place when it comes to a good mixture of pedestrians, metros, buses, cars, taxis, bicycles, motor scooters, and I guess, soon enough "Segways". Amsterdam is an old city. Austin is old for Texas but not in comparison to other great world cities. Amsterdam and Paris were laid out when there were only horses and oxen pulling carts. And they were not really laid out. The roads or paths just appeared. That's why they aren't straight or parallel. When the buildings came, they appeared alongside of the road. Thus, you have narrow streets in the Medieval Quarters of Paris and Barcelona and Istanbul, and Beijing.

In Austin, except for Barton Springs Road which actually crosses with Riverside, our streets are pretty predictable. The unthinkable confusion of two streets not really staying put where a particular street is south of another, then it is not, must rarely be negotiated by the orthogonal mind of most Austinites. Our streets were planned with trees (now numbers) running east-west and the rivers running north-south. They are reasonably wide even though the automobile was still three generations away when the town was founded along with the Republic of Texas in 1836.

Transportation shapes Cities. Paris looks the way it does because of transportation. Yes, there was some serious planning and urban renewal during the second empire of Napoleon II when the Baron Von Hausemann tore up the streets and created the grand boulevards such as the Champs-Elysees. But the Rue de Le Tombs is where it is because that's how Parisians got their dead to the cemetery.

Most of the great cities in the US have grown up since the automobile. And they show it. The newer cities in the West are the worst. LA, Houston, and Phoenix are literally all over the map.

But not only does transportation shape cities, energy policy shapes cities. And this country does have an energy policy. The policy is inexpensively priced energy. Notice I said price, not cost. Inexpensively priced gasoline creates flat, spread out cities that use even more energy. Each person in the US averages around 10,870 km of city driving a year. Compare this with Western Europe averages of less than 5,000 and averages of less than 2,000 km in developed Asia. In Western Europe, 42% of the people drive to work or wherever, 39% use public transport, and 18% walk or cycle to work. In developed Asia, 20% drive a car, 60% use public transport, and 20% walk or cycle. The averages in the US are strikingly different. In the US, 86% drive, 9% use public transit, and less than 5% walk or cycle. Some studies now indicate that the real costs of automobile dependence outweigh the economic benefits of car transportation. Real estate analysts have come to see that denser cities that have alternatives to the car are better investment bets than sprawling suburban areas.

And there is a human element that cannot be quantified. In the United States, transportation deaths are the highest in the World at 14.6 deaths per 100 thousand. Western Europe suffers 8.8 deaths/100,000 and developed Asia suffers 6.6 deaths. Worldwide traffic deaths are almost a million a year. That is one city the size of Austin lost every year.

In Austin, 99% of transportation CO_2 emissions come from private vehicles and air travel. Public transport accounts for less than 1%. Those of us who walk or bicycle to work number slightly more than 10,000 according to the census bureau. Of the half million workers, that would mean 2% use human power to get there. Western European cities have almost 20%. Public ridership in Austin is less than 40,000 a day. That is slightly less than the US average and 1/4 of the European city average.

"Necessity Never Made a Good Bargain"

If a community or city is indeed a living system and the transportation system is its circulatory system, and that system provides the food and oxygen for the other organs of the body, then our present auto dominated system with a body that is literally "all over the map" presents special challenges and opportunities.

What we think we want may not be what we need and what we need may not be what we think.

Technology can indeed influence our cities and how we transport ourselves and the goods and materials that must flow through them. The need for couriers is arguably reduced by fax machines and e-mail. The telephone reduces the amount of trips you need to take almost anywhere. The Yellow Pages still promotes "let your fingers do the walking." If someone invented a dematerializer that worked like the transporters on Star Trek, you could say goodbye to highways, trains, planes, and cities as we know them. Probably not going to happen this week. But the point is this, advanced technology can make surprising and dramatic changes in the way we live and the way our cities and communities develop and thrive. Look at what the car and the internal combustion engine have accomplished in less than 100 years! Roads and parking lots devour as much as 1/3 of the land of car reliant cities.

Austin is one of 79 cities in the US committed to developing local strategies to combat global warming. The Austin Carbon Dioxide Reduction Strategy for the transportation sector focuses on reducing Vehicle Miles Traveled (VMT). It contemplates decreasing the use of single-occupant vehicles. According to the report, this can be achieved by promoting:

Carpooling

Telecommuting

Work schedule changes

Vanpooling

Increased public transit ridership

Land use strategies can also be employed that increase the number of people who choose to walk or ride a bicycle to work. Lockers and showers in the workplace would help.

Initiated in 1995 when Austin became an energy smart city by resolution of the City Council, these efforts have resulted with daily average VMT in Travis County increasing from 17,698,000 to 20,078,000. As the January 2001 update of the City of Austin Carbon Dioxide Strategy states regarding transportation, "we are not only behind schedule, but are actually moving in the wrong direction. Achieving this goal is technically possible, but will require dramatic changes."

If the Citizens of Austin are going to create a robust circulation system for our community body that is healthy, economic, efficient, and nonpolluting, and hopefully fun and exciting, we need to act now and not after we are faced with regulatory remedies that limit our opportunities or curtail our imaginations. We all know you can't borrow money when you're broke or make new friends when you are needy. Do we really need dramatic changes in our lifestyles or dramatic revisioning of our lifestyle?

Are there solutions waiting for us that are just outside of the current box of public discourse or even just on the next page if we would only turn it?

It doesn't really matter whether we live in a gated community in the Hill Country and believe that the real problem is not enough roads with enough lanes, or we live in central Austin and believe that the real problem is no viable public transportation: WE ALL HATE SITTING IN TRAFFIC.

Sitting in traffic is a colossal waste of time and, in our fast paced economy, a waste of money. As Franklin said, "Time is money." Specifically, in the US alone, it is estimated that wasted fuel and productivity in the metro areas costs 74 billion dollars annually.

The solution from the Right is to build more roads. The solution from the Left is to limit growth. The battle that ensues is not truly constructive. The battleground is not just the wrong ground. It's like fighting for freedom in the wrong century. What's the purpose?

We want neighborhoods that are safe. Whether we live in the inner city or the suburbs, we want a sense of community. Most of us would like to walk to the corner store and get some milk without starting our cars. Most of us would like for the kids to run around the neighborhood without fear. Most of us would like to know our neighbors. Whether we own a Chevy Suburban or a Geo Metro, we are united by these and many other common needs and desires. How do we take these commonalities and forge them into a vision of transportation efficiency and land use optimization that provides the opportunity to realize them?

THE VISION OF VISION

As the ads say, Austin is a City of Ideas. We don't have to settle for traffic jams and pollution. We are a rich and modern city with a young and creative high tech mentality.

If we are to build a World Class City, we must develop World Class Attitude.

The other night, I was visiting with a downtown lawyer from one of those firms with lots of floors, offices all over Texas, hundreds of lawyers, and plenty of clients to keep them all busy. We began to visit about the Community of the Future Initiative.

He volunteered that what we really need to do is build an underground metro. He argued that there is truly no world-class city without one. He is right. There is no world-class city that does not have an underground metro. There is a lot of real estate down there.

> *"We are ready for an unforeseen event*
> *that may or may not occur."*
>
> *Al Gore*

But if we can't agree to build a light rail, how could we agree to build a true metro? Perhaps because the citizens of Austin believe that in this case an ounce of prevention is just an ounce of cure. There is nothing wrong with light rail. <u>Dallas</u> is enjoying success with its system. <u>Portland</u> is expanding their system. There are many good reasons to move forward with the plan now. Perhaps we will. But we will need more. As Yogi Berra says, "When you come to a fork in the road, take it."

One camp might argue that our planners are too short-sighted or maybe too cautious. And in all fairness, that caution could hardly be characterized as ill placed. Perhaps the Citizens of Austin want a more visionary long-term approach that truly builds a great city. There are many new systems and combinations of technologies. Instead of going down and below, we could go up like Chicago did during the early part of the last century and like Seattle is doing now as it expands its monorail system. If we went up, thrilled riders would be afforded spectacular views of the hill country and skyline. We can go up with heavy monorail tracks or with lighter rails that accommodate smaller cars. Smaller technologies are more modular and more responsive to the changes in growth and preference that each section of the city inevitably cycles through.

There is developing technology that uses much smaller carriages called personal rapid transit. These PRT technologies are not currently operational or even ready for deployment. They generally carry four or fewer people on an elevated guideway with off-line stations. Active proposals to apply the PRT concept are found in the Cities 21 project in the Silicon Valley of California, and the Skyloop project in Cincinnati, Ohio. We could opt to create a system of elevated walkways for walkers, cyclists, and lightweight electric vehicles. These skyways could link the inner city into a tight knit community totally accessible by human power. There is even an enclosed wind blown version of this concept called BTS TransGlide 2000. It claims that people and freight can be transported at speeds faster than light rail, buses, or motor vehicles. Its proponents claim that it actually pays for itself without large public subsidies.

We could opt to move toward an all-electric bus system of trollycoaches that run on renewable energy at a fraction of light rail costs. The buses could be electrified via overhead lines or with batteries or both. They could be fuel cell vehicles running on hydrogen. These buses could have designated lanes and boarding stations. Routes could be redesigned to facilitate different trip strategies. Such hub and spoke routes could drastically change ridership profiles. This kind of repackaged bus system is now beginning to catch more and more attention. Now called Bus Rapid Transit, the concept was pioneered in Brazil in Curitiba where a staggering 70% of the work force uses the Bus Transit System. Recently, Federal Transportation Authorities have indicated their approval of BRT systems.

Today, Capital Metro is expecting two hybrid diesel vehicles to add to their fleet of approximately 300 buses. Most of them are once again diesel. The mechanics and management of Capital Metro have not accepted the clean burning natural gas engines that were brought in during the nineties. Perhaps 37,000,000 passenger boardings occurred last year.

A great city needs a large portfolio of transportation options.

After my 5th or 6th trip to Paris, I realized that there was an entire level of transportation underneath the Metro I had grown so accustomed to. The RER, for Rapid something or another, will whisk you from Le Defense, in the far West side of town to the Louvre in a matter of minutes at high speed. It will run you out deep into the suburbs and countryside with a minimum of stops. When you get to the general area you are going to in the city, you go up to the metro level where you take the subway to get you even closer. Then, you go up to the surface and walk, cab, or bus to your final destination. Paris has three distinct spacial levels of transportation. As long as no one is on strike, the system works and it works well. At any one time during a normal weekday, it is estimated that 1 million people are in the underground with more than that at rush hour.

The big excitement in train travel is magnetic levitation or Maglev. One such project is the Baltimore Washington project. It is one of two national finalists for this technology in the United States. Internationally, the Maglev project that will be the first to operate commercially will be in China. The Transrapid will begin service between Pudong Shanghai Airport and the Shanghai financial district in the beginning of 2003. There are Magplanes concepts that float in a trough of magnets and jet-like airtrains that hang on a fixed rail. Both of these technologies have carriages that more resemble small corporate jets. Their speeds are faster than the fastest fast trains in Europe.

There is a Maglev project in California, which is supported by the Governor and most Californians. Governor Davis even had to veto an anti-Maglev bill. Recently the program received 1 million in federal appropriations. There is another high-speed rail project in Colorado. However, the preponderance of rail projects, whether light, heavy, maglev, or high speed are not in the US. They are in Europe and in the Far East.

There are also developing technologies that use air to propel the carriage. One such automated people mover called Aeromovel claims capital low cost, high performance, easy and fast implementation, environmental compatibility, and reliability through its pneumatic propulsion system. There is a similar elevated system called Whoosh that runs on air propulsion or what the developers call an atmospheric engine. These systems can be very fast, very quiet, and very efficient with modern space age carriages that are light and safe. They hang or travel on elevated rails that are engineered to support these lighter loads thus further reducing costs and visual concerns.

Other developing technologies include evacuated tube technologies that boast travel speeds of 4000 miles per hour. These technologies are feasible, yet because of perception and institutional biases, these advanced approaches remain distant from general acceptance and are far from deployment into the public infrastructure.

"The present is the ever-moving shadow that divides yesterday from tomorrow. In that lies hope."

Frank Lloyd Wright

If you have ever attended a debate on light rail or any discussion on mass transportation, one thing is for sure. These people know what they are talking about and they are very committed to their ideas and positions. Unfortunately, they don't agree. In the Light Rail debate in Austin, the phrase "Costs too much, Does too little" decimated the pro Rail advocates in the last election. South Congress merchants are not anxious to trade in their livelihoods for a public transit construction project that may or may not work and they have organized against it. This is more than ironic. These are the very people and well thinking citizens of Austin who could be leading the charge for a compact livable city. Their position is the equivalent of musicians voting for sound ordinances on Sixth Street.

Their position, however, is totally rational. Their businesses will suffer in a major construction project that disrupts South Congress and they need to be compensated for that loss.

Talk to anyone about Capital Metro and you will get a rise in blood pressure. Even with a new board structure and leadership, Cap Metro has been hard pressed to recast its image. Everyone seems to have his or her private ideas on how to fix it. No one has yet.

BACK TO THE FUTURE

When cars first appeared on the scene at the turn of the 20th century many were electric. With the advent of an internal combustion engine that was dependable, <u>electric cars</u> disappeared.

Now they are almost back.

As much as we hear about fuel cells and zero emission vehicles, they are remarkably few and far between. Try to buy one here in Texas. California, because of its zero emission mandate is changing this. Ford was offering a small electric car called "<u>The Think</u>". Now they have a new concept vehicle called the <u>model "U"</u>. There are actually just a handful of electric vehicles in Austin. Daimler Chrysler is coming out with its "Smart". You can order it from the web in Europe, but not in the US. Toyota will be offering its RAV4 in California only. There is a cute three-wheeled vehicle called a "<u>Sparrow</u>". It comes in a dozen or so colors and it is well designed. It makes the point in its web site that 87% of US commuters travel 18 miles or less to work daily, and 93% do so alone. This vehicle can get you there and back for about a penny.

Honda has announced that it will offer a <u>hydrogen powered fuel cell vehicle</u> within the next year. Even though there is a limited, almost nonexistent infrastructure for such a vehicle, the company insists that the vehicle will be offered. Most major automakers are developing fuel cell vehicles. Few are scheduled to hit the market anytime soon.

There is another breed of car that is hitting the market. These cars are <u>hybrids</u>. They are half electric and half I.C.E. They operate on the principle that a smaller highly tuned internal combustion engine running at constant speed is more efficient than an engine that accelerates up and down. Often, the constant speed engine keeps batteries charged that provide electricity to an electric motor. Some strategies provide direct power to the drivetrain and use the electric motor for acceleration. Most hybrids convert braking energy into usable motive energy through their generators. The two most successful hybrids on the market are the Toyota Prius and the Honda Insight. Both get around 50 miles to a gallon of gasoline. Such cars, like all internal combustion cars, could also run directly on hydrogen. A former mayor of Austin drives a red Insight today.

The Rocky Mountain Institute believes strongly that their Hypercar concept is the right approach. These cars would have superior aerodynamics, superior weight ratios through the use of advanced composite materials, and hybrid or fuel cell powered drive trains. They believe they can achieve miles per gallon ratios approaching 100.

There are electric scooters and electric bikes. There are electric skateboards and probably some electric skates somewhere. (I haven't seen them yet.) Then there is the revolutionary Kamen and his Segway. This personal transportation device looks more like a push mower. You stand on it, change your center of gravity, and it will respond almost mystically to your subtle commands. Lean forward and away you go. Lean or pull back and you stop or go in reverse. Will our cities be full of these personal transportation devices in the next 10 years? It is easy to say that things change very slowly. The ferriers of the 19th century had known job security for thousands of years. The horse was the only reliable way to travel. Only within the last 100 years has that not been the case. We as a highly developed technological culture still measure units of power in horsepower and units of energy in horsepower hours. The change from horses to horsepower occurred in the proverbial blink of an eye. Horseshoes were replaced by rubber tires and inner tubes. Will the car, which has so clearly dominated our cities and our culture, experience the same demise?

One of the joys of a great city is the ability to walk. Whether it is a village in New England or the Village in New York, walking is the transportation backbone of any great community. Great streets make for great walking. Walking through the neighborhoods in Paris, you come upon a cheese shop, a chocolate shop, then a Brasserie. Windows are dressed for the eyes of the walker. Even with the domination of the car, the walker is still of stature in Paris and other great cities. New York is one of the great battlegrounds of this conflict. Just last year Mayor Giulliani tried to make jaywalking a crime. It was unenforceable.

"If we don't succeed, we run the risk of failure."

THE UNIFIED ENERGY SYSTEM

When the University of Texas plays football in the fall of each year, perhaps 30,000 vehicles are parked in order for the 84,000 fans to come to Memorial Stadium. If each car has 200 horsepower, then approximately 6 million horsepower is parked during that 4-hour game period. That represents about 4500 megawatts of power potential. The City of Austin has about 2500 megawatts of electrical generation potential. There is a larger power plant in the parking lots in and around the stadium for those four hours than in all the generation capacity found in our coal plants, our share of the South Texas Nuclear Plant, our gas plants, and wind fields. There are 1,178,593 vehicles registered in Austin. We don't have that many people.

Let's assume that a hybrid-electric vehicle has a 50 horsepower engine and a generator and motor to match. It may or may not run on hydrogen. Or assume we have a fuel cell vehicle with a 37 KW fuel stack. Now assume that 10% of the registered vehicles in the city were such vehicles. Those 117,000 vehicles could provide about 4,000 megawatts of electrical capacity. The issue here is not one which asks the question "why do we not use the excess power capacity of our cars to power our homes and offices?" but rather the question we should ask is " why can't we use our cars to power our homes and offices if we want to, or when we must?" Why are the two systems, our transportation power system and our electrical power system "noncompatible?"

It's as if one is a Mac and the other is a PC.

A unification of these two systems would provide substantial value to the overall energy infrastructure. Transportation power plants could be used to shore up electrical generation shortfalls during peak periods of use during a heat storm in August, or for emergencies during an ice storm in January, or a thunderstorm in May.

A unified energy system would allow homeowners to power their homes with their cars by charging up battery banks. Such a house would not only be self-sufficient, it would have numerous powering options. Solar powered homes with a unified energy strategy could reduce the size of the photovoltaic array and/or omit back up generation.

All electric vehicles achieve this unification. The owner of an electric vehicle can charge his or her car from green power from West Texas wind farms, with brown power from the Fayette coal plant, with their own photovoltaic systems, or with local back up generation that runs on natural gas, propane, or hydrogen. Whether the vehicle uses batteries or fuel cells is a non-issue on this strategic issue. The systems can and should be unified. Unification will reduce costs by reducing society's total investment. It will increase reliability. It will create a better market. It will provide an avenue for independence.

The unification of our transportation power infrastructure with the electric grid that powers our homes and businesses would significantly alter the energy landscape and the way we operate in it.

NEVER CONFUSE MOTION WITH ACTION

What does this mean? What was the wily Ben Franklin telling us?

Let's go back to my Interstate Highway breakfast. The raisin bran may be the most obvious here. Grain is grown in the Midwest with fertilizer from natural gas from Canada to Mexico. It is shipped to the East where it is milled and cooked and packaged probably on trains that might run on diesel from Venezuela. Then, it is sent in trucks driving on Mexican diesel to distribution centers ultimately ending up in the Whole Foods Market where I pick it up and drive it home in my Chevy.

From a market perspective this is all very efficient. There is a great deal of motion and a modest amount of action. I get cereal. It is fresh enough I suppose. From an energy perspective, it is a colossal waste of resources.

As long as energy is priced low, this works. If the price were high, the market would respond differently. Local mills and local manufacturers would have a proverbial leg up with high transportation costs. Cereal from the East Coast would not make a lot of sense.

Why do Austinites drive 20,000,000 miles a day? That's forty miles a day for each of us.

One reason is the way we have built our city. Since most of the city has been developed in the last 50 years, we have a car dependent architecture. But another perhaps more powerful reason is psychological. We like to get out. We like to get out and drive. Those ad men who told us to "See the USA in your Chevrolet" knew what they were saying. It taps into a basic American and human need.

That basic human need is Freedom. Cars provide the closest thing many of us know to it. Ask your teenager. We cannot and should not underestimate the power of that need.

I began to walk and use cabs instead of driving several years ago because I felt more free. Being free of a car and the need to find a parking space became more important than having my car at my immediate disposal. Being free from the tyranny of having to drive became a more powerful expression of freedom. The ability to walk from the cab door to the front door of the State Capitol became a symbol of power. The spring day walk through the University of Texas back to my home and office became more of a luxury than knowing I could whistle Trigger to my rescue. Besides, I did know where Trigger was stabled.

This kind of attitude is just coming of age. In Europe, car sharing is becoming acceptable. There is a car-sharing program in Portland. Cab companies could find that Executive Cab services with automatic billing services and cell phone access would be considered more environmental and even more chic than driving your Buick to the office tower garage where it lays fallow all day. With home or office delivery and expedited transaction times, rental car companies could find that there is a market in the suburbs for rental cars for travel, for weekends, for special purposes, for odd jobs, and other special vehicle needs or enjoyments. Many two or three-car families could find that one car is enough when executive cab services, expedited car rentals, and improved public transit is considered and available.

The point is, we drive 20,000,000 miles a day for more reasons than we perhaps know. We could call to check to see if the Home Depot has a new drill on sale. We could check out that new house that just came on the market by looking at the pictures on the web, but we want to see it. We want to touch it. We are programmed to get as much sensory information as we can before we make a decision.

The same issues that exist in our buying habits exist when it comes to our work. As much as we say we would like to work at home, most telecommuters feel isolated when they don't come into the office. They miss the gossip, the chitchat, and the human interaction that occurs at the office. This can be replaced somewhat with sophisticated video conferencing, video e-mail, and screen sharing, and more sophisticated conferencing programs that provide for more group interaction through split screening. Maybe a web cam of the coffee bar and the waiting lounge would go a long way. The more information and stimulus, the better the telecommuter will feel and the better informed he or she will be.

The Austin Carbon Dioxide Reduction Strategy Update estimates that less than 10,000 workers telecommute. This number could be dramatically increased. A study by Apogee concludes that 10% of the work force could be telecommuting. That would represent 50,000 workers. The aggressive scenario found in the CO_2 report assumes 85,000 telecommuters. This kind of acceptance would reduce CO_2 emissions by more than 170,000 tons a year. Advanced telecommuting could make this number even higher. Clearly, employers and employees would need to foster a significant change in relationship and empowerment for this to occur.

We should not confuse Motion with Action.

Motion is tapping your fingers. Action is typing with your fingers.

Motion is driving to work. Action is the drive to work.

I had a political mentor many years ago that told me to never confuse effort with result.

We used to get in the car and just drive around and talk.

"Any sufficiently advanced technology is indistinguishable from magic."

Arthur C. Clark

Chapter Five

Energy *and* Persistence Conquer *all* Things

Technology Review *of* New Technologies

"When I was young I observed that nine out of ten things
I did were failures, so I did ten times more work."

Bernard Shaw

The Renewable Energy Industry is by most standards a very young and immature industry. There have been technological failures and bankruptcies. There have been claims and expectations.

Years ago, when the industry was not sure which wind technology would become the standard, I ran into the director of the Alcoa Wind Program. Alcoa, at the time, was invested in the Darrius wind concept. These turbines had great advantages. They were vertical axis turbines. They could be manufactured on a large scale at a relatively low cost. They could be serviced from the ground. They were the newest advancement in wind conversion technologies. Even the highly regarded NASA had helped develop their design.

Apparently, his press people had arranged to start a large 500 KW machine in California in front of the press and politicians. Somehow, his plane was late. While heading to the site, he was chatting with his cabby. "Did you hear about the wind mill that destroyed itself in front of the press today" his cabby shared. "What kind of Turbine?" "One of those new-fangled ones." A lump formed in Paul's throat and then settled deep in his stomach. I would imagine it would be much like heading to the hospital after you've been told that a loved one was in a bad car accident.

You know it's going to be bad, you just can't imagine how bad.

Vertical Axis turbines died that day. Oh, there were a few more attempts to prove that the technology would work. Here in Texas, The Alternative Energy Institute installed a couple of them on their test bed outside of Amarillo. They would be memorials to a young and immature industry.

Before that, in the early eighties, there was an innovative father and son team here in Texas that took the skills that they had developed in the fiber wound pipe business and in helicopter blade design and applied them to this young industry. They designed a down-wind, two-blade wind generator that held great promise in the early eighties. Using the Carter technology, one early plant in the Texas panhandle consisting of five 25 KW machines was installed at the amazing cost of 70 cents a Watt.

At one time, this unit with its lightweight design and tilt down tower looked as if it would become the standard in the wind farms of America. United Technologies had a similar unit. Another design from Lubbock and Texas Tech also held promise.

During this time, corporate engineering giants like Boeing and Hamilton Standard were designing and building using development grants from DOE to test wind turbines that were 1 or 2 megawatts in size. They were two-bladed behemoths that would never work very well. The Europeans, mostly the Danes, were producing wind generators that were fairly straightforward. They faced the wind, so there was no tower shadow loads to manage. They had three blades instead of two. They were strong and heavy. They appeared in the California wind fields in sizes of 60 to 90 KW. Then, they grew to 120 KW. The Carter Turbine grew to the remarkable scale of 250 KW. But it would continue to have difficulties. As the nineties came along, Vestas, a European company, became a world leader as they leaped to 600 KW. Today, the Texas wind fields are made up primarily of units of one megawatt or more. That is the size that was incomprehensible and totally ridiculous just 20 years back. The winner of the technology war was the straightforward European design. Everybody else is Beta Max.

Now, there are 3 and even 5-megawatt machines in the works.

In the span of 20 years, wind technology had grown from house size units of 25 KW to utility scale units of 2.5 MW. A farmer can put in a field of 25 or 50 KW machines, but 1 MW machines require cranes, lawyers, and interconnect agreements. As it has matured, the wind industry has become a utility scale business. Today the price of wind with federal production credits is less than 3 cents. That is below the utility fuel costs of many natural gas plants. Indeed, two gas plants in Texas are now running as load following units that work in tandem with the wind facilities that surround them. It is cheaper to run the wind than to run the gas plant.

The City of Austin gets its electricity from wind power from a high mesa just north of McCamey, Texas. This "state of the industry" facility has windwalls of 30-story, 1 MW wind turbines running across the edges of this 500-foot mesa. For now, it is part of the largest wind plant in the world. It is half the size of a big coal plant.

The growth of the wind industry in the United States and the world is truly impressive. Wind Power is the fastest growing source of electrical power there is. The web sites of the American Wind Energy Association and the European Wind Energy Association tell their stories well.

There are approximately 30,000 Megawatts of wind power in the world today. In Texas, we now have approximately 1100 of those megawatts. In 2001, only Germany and Spain installed more wind power than Texas. The wind fleet in Texas represents some of the most modern and cost effective generation available today.

"We are confronted with insurmountable opportunities."

Walt Kelly

WIND IN THE FUTURE

Wind power in Texas has enormous potential. At present that potential is constricted by the transmission capability leading from the resource in the west to the demand found in the cities to the east.

As the wind industry matures, there may be resources offshore that may prove to be as attractive as they are now in Europe. The recent announcements of lighter, stronger towers will also expand the range of good resource. Tower heights of over 100 meters will open up wind regimes closer to Austin just to the west and to the south. These developments are imminent and should be considered in near term planning efforts.

SOLAR ENERGY

Wouldn't it be great if we could take the energy that strikes our house everyday and use it to run our air conditioning during the day and our lights and entertainment appliances at night? It's just the opposite of the cartoon in which the house needs more and more electricity to run the air conditioner because it's getting hotter and hotter from climate change. Meanwhile, the power plant providing the electricity is belching more and more CO_2 into environment, which is causing more and more warming and the need for more air conditioning, and so on, and so on. In the solar scenario, the more sunlight you use, the less you have warming your house, the less electricity you need to cool it, and on and on. It's what scientists call positive feedback.

So why don't all of our houses and buildings have solar electric panels and solar hot water panels neatly imbedded into their roofs providing all the electricity and hot water the house or office needs?

It costs too much.

The photovoltaic effect was actually predicted by Albert Einstein early in the last century. Bell Labs finally made one work by the

1950s. Initially, they were used to power satellites. By the late 70s, we began to see some here on Earth. Today, we see them everywhere if you know where to look and what they look like. You see them at school crossings powering the warning lights. You see them on those trailers with the big arrows that tell you to merge right in a construction zone. They power hand held calculators quite nicely. In the countryside, they are used to monitor all kinds of things, from the flow of gas in a pipeline to the measuring of the amount of wind at a potential wind site. Along our freeways and walking trails, they power our emergency phone stations. There are also thousands of remote homes and cottages that use them because the grid is too far away or the owner wants nothing to do with the electric company.

Like the wind industry, the solar industry is a very young industry. True, inventors have been trying to harness the sun for thousands of years. Da Vinci had drawings and began building a burning lens in 1515. More than two thousand years ago, legend has it that Archimedes used mirrors to destroy the Roman Fleet. The Frenchman, Mouchot, invented the first solar engine just as the Confederates were bombarding Ft. Sumter.

In the late 1980s, Luz International produced solar electricity from their plants in the desert of California for around 10 cents/KWh. These plants are still operational today. These plants heated oil using focusing reflective troughs. The super-heated oil then created the steam. This strategy allowed for the plant to be co-fired with natural gas and other fuels.

There are many ways to take solar energy and make it useful. You can hang your laundry on a 49-cent clothesline and use it to dry your clothes, thus reducing your need for electricity. You can build a house that is sensitive to the sun and its position throughout the seasons. You can use it to make <u>hot water</u>. You can do that with an active collector that has a pump or with a batch heater that preheats your water before it goes into the hot water heater. That batch heater can be a black waterbed on your roof or a sophisticated copper serpentine unit that works in the winter too.

Solar is good for heating water and we in the West certainly spend a lot of energy heating water for our showers, our baths, and washing our clothes. Hospitals and hotels use lots of hot water. I presume you are guilty of using the hotel shower to press your clothes too.

We can also use solar collectors that make hot water to produce air-conditioning. The process is well understood but generally not employed. Air conditioning is a substantial part of electrical demand.

Standard one-sun solar photovoltaics can be installed on the roof of a house or warehouse with relative ease. Other approaches, which concentrate the sun, can also be utilized. The strategies can be more efficient and less costly, but they generally require some kind of tracking of the sun. This complicates the installation. Solar generation, in general, can be installed at the house level, the neighborhood level, or at the bulk power level. Bulk power strategies are often more cost effective. Power Tower strategies with their rows and rows of heliostats have often evoked predictions of 5-cent solar electricity. They have not delivered those kinds of cost efficiencies yet. Yet, there is no fundamental reason why this University of Houston technology cannot be developed to produce cost effective solar energy.

The truth is, the Luz plants, developed almost 20 years ago, are still the most successful, proven solar electric generation stations (SEGS) on a utility scale.

Lately, The National Renewable Energy Lab, which is the leading government research and development facility for Renewable Energy development, has once again embraced the notion of focusing PV's as a viable strategy for reducing costs. NREL has an impressive array of photovoltaic products and processes that can be licensed. However, the photovoltaic industry, those manufacturers and representatives who have and who are producing product that can be warranted for 20 or more years, is selling a product that produces electricity for over 20 cents KWh. Prices per KW are trending towards 3 dollars/watt, but they need to be closer to one dollar for cost-effective large-scale deployment to occur. The City of Austin's most recent purchase of photovoltaics is a testament to the continued reduction of PV prices in general. The PV industry, like the Wind industry is beginning to mature.

In determining the wisdom of any technology that is to be deployed on a large scale, the concept of energy recapture must be considered. It simply makes no sense to embrace a technology that cannot capture and deliver more usable energy than it takes to create it.

In the early days of the oil boom, this ratio of "energy returned" to "energy invested" was over 30 to 1. Today, that ratio is closer to 10 to 1. Wind turbines are now providing energy returns in that same range. Consequently, the prices for wind-generated electricity are competitive with the fossil market.

Currently, crystalline PV technologies have energy ratios that range from a low of 2 to 1 to a high of about 4 to 1. Thin film technologies range in the area of 5 to 1. Once 10 to 1 ratios are achieved, large-scale deployment of PV can be considered. Multi-sun strategies have the potential to increase the energy ratio beyond the 10 to 1 threshold. These ratios are also dependent on where they are located. A dry hole in the oil business has a negative energy ratio. A one-megawatt wind turbine in Austin, Texas would have a very small return on energy invested. Solar installed in Austin will perform well, but not as good as a system installed in El Paso.

Just 30 years ago, PVs cost over 50 dollars a Watt. Today, they are pushing 3 dollars/ Watt. Twenty years ago, the PV industry shipped not quite a megawatt a year worldwide. Today, the industry ships almost 400 MWs annually with 700 MWs a year projected by 2005. That is the equivalent of a large coal plant every year.

THE SOLAR FUTURE

The National Renewable Energy Lab predicts that PV costs will approach one dollar/Watt in the next 10 years. If this prediction is correct, Distributed Solar Energy for electrical generation will become a viable option.

There are significant developments around the world which might even crash through the one dollar/Watt threshold. Using the developing sciences of nanotechnology, carbon based PVs may someday soon hold the promise of large scale solar generation. Using Nanotubes, researchers at Cambridge University envision carbon solar surfaces that take a variety of shapes and patterns. University of California Berkeley chemists have found a way to make plastic solar cells flexible enough to paint onto any surface and potentially able to provide electricity from wearable electric generators. Others are using Titania dye.

One thing is clear.

The PV industry is on the verge of achieving cost efficiencies that will make distributed solar generation a viable alternative to fossil fuel generation. The question is not so much if, but when, and what? Meanwhile, the PV industry continues to grow and mature and ship more product at more affordable prices. However, in order to become competitive and a strategy for large-scale deployment, prices must still be at least halved and energy ratios must be at least doubled.

This is not true of large-scale solar projects such as the Luz International Plants. Solar Energy Generation Stations are capable now of producing electricity in the 9 to 10 cent range. With a national commitment, large-scale solar plants could be competitive today in the 5 to 7 cent range. Technologies, which employ unique solar strategies such as power towers and hemispheric moving focus can produce bulk power economically and exhibit highly favorable energy ratios approaching 10 to 1.

For Austin, where a reasonably good solar resource improves as you move west and south by several hundreds of miles, a strategy that includes a combination of bulk, neighborhood, and building generation seems appropriate due to the inherent strength and security of such a broad-based solar portfolio.

New generation solar plants and cells will allow much of Austin's generation growth to be met by these technologies. Austin Energy should take the lead in developing these technologies not only for its stockholder/citizens but also for markets and utilities outside of the Austin area. An Austin Energy advanced in these technologies would be capable of maximizing its own resources and profitability. Such profitability could actually reduce rates for Citizens while providing a long-term sustainable strategy.

BIOGAS and BIOMASS

The biogas industry is actually a by-product of regulation. When the Environmental Protection Agency ruled that the natural methane that was drifting up from our decomposing landfills should and must be managed, a nice benefit became obvious. Instead of allowing these gases to rise up and collect in homes or in the environment, this gas could be burned in large reciprocating engines which turned generators which could be used by the utility company to meet its load requirements. Truly, waste became a resource. Today, Austin Energy, in conjunction with its development vendors, is actively seeking to harness this resource for the good of Austin's citizenry. Electricity from this source is reliable and economic, but it is limited in its capacity. Most projects expect to produce electricity in the 5 to 6 cent range when federal credits are included.

Other biogas projects from animal waste in rural areas could also provide usable fuel for electrical generation. There are extensive confined animal feeding operations in the state that can have their waste converted into usable energy. However, these projects will not be realized as long as the environment is a free dump for these wastes. Once water resources become more valuable than the free dump resource, these wastes will be managed and converted. The total resource potential, although significant, is limited in meeting the growth of Austin Energy and the combined electrical generation growth of Texas. According to a report of the Sustainable Energy Development Council of Texas, all municipal sewage, animal waste, and landfills have an annual potential of .12 quads. That is just slightly more than the amount of energy the utility uses now to generate the 10,000 Gigawatts hours that is presently consumed.

Perhaps the most elegant solar strategy of all is right below our feet. Plain old dirt, water, and sunlight make for a very cost-effective solar energy conversion device. In fact, there is a fairly mature industry built around the idea. It's called agriculture.

The fact is, when it comes to growing things to burn and not eat, conversion efficiencies of solar energy to biomass are low, but who cares. I sometimes wonder, if we could just grind up every weed that grows in between the cracks of my driveway and blow it into a furnace that produced steam that turned a turbine that produced electricity, surely our energy needs would be solved.

Biomass can and could provide the fuel for our electrical needs. But, it takes a large area to provide large amounts of fuel. Providing a third of Austin Energy's fuel through biomass would require approximately 130,000 acres. That area of 200 square miles is roughly the size of Austin. To provide the same amount of energy with solar would require 4,000 acres. To provide the energy through wind plants would require 22,000 acres.

According to the SEDC Renewable Energy Assessment Report, Texas has 250 quads of solar energy that is accessible, 4 quads of wind energy, 3 quads of biomass, 1 quad each of water and geothermal and 1/4 of a quad in building climatology.

Presently, Texas consumes 12 quads of energy. Half of that is consumed by Industry. Three quads are used in the electric sector and 2 1/2 quads are used in the transportation sector.

FUEL CELLS AND MICROTURBINES

Fuel Cell technology is developing rapidly. The fuel cell industry is working to perfect cell stacks that work in both stationary and mobile applications. Some companies like Plug Power hope to provide fuel cells for the home that operate outside the home much like a standard air-conditioning unit. Other companies like Ballard are working on transportation applications. Fuel cells are clean and silent. They are still too expensive and the stacks have longevity problems. One of the most promising uses of fuel cells is in the small power pack area.

The principle behind fuel cells was discovered in 1839. However, using fuel cells as electricity generation devices dates back only a few decades when NASA began using the technology in the United States space program. Fuel cells provided power for on-board electronics for the Gemini and Apollo spacecrafts, and still provide electricity and water for the space shuttle today.

What is a Fuel Cell?

A fuel cell is a device that converts the energy of a fuel (hydrogen, natural gas, methanol, gasoline, etc.) and an oxidant (air or oxygen) into useable electricity. Fuel cell construction generally consists of a fuel electrode (anode) and an oxidant electrode (cathode) separated by an ion conducting membrane.

Types of Fuel Cells

There are several different types of fuel cells, including phosphoric acid, alkaline, molten carbonate, solid oxide and PEM (proton exchange membrane) fuel cells. Plug Power believes PEM fuel cells can be manufactured less expensively and are more efficient and more practical in small-scale applications. These cells operate at relatively low temperatures (under 200°F/93°C), have high power density, and can vary their output quickly to meet shifts in power demand.

Unlike traditional fossil plants that combust fuels, fuel cells generate electricity through an electrochemical process from which no particulate matter, nitrogen or sulfur oxides (NOx or SOx) are produced. As a result, they do not contribute to the formation of smog and acid rain. Furthermore, a significant percentage of heat produced by fuel cells can be captured and reused, instead of being released into the air or water, as is the common practice with large central station generating plants.

In the summer of 2002, Austin Energy installed a 200 KW fuel cell on a commercial facility. Costs for this demonstration were more than 5 dollars a watt, roughly the present cost of solar PV.

A reversible fuel cell that provides energy on peak and stores off peak energy as hydrogen and oxygen would be of maximum value to an electric utility that wishes to make the most out of its renewable resources and existing generation assets.

Microturbines are a new type of combustion turbine being used for stationary energy generation applications. They are small combustion turbines, approximately the size of a refrigerator, with outputs of 25 KW to 500 KW, and can be located on sites with space limitations for power production. Ironically, they were originally developed as power plants for the aviation industry. Microturbines are composed of a compressor, combustor, turbine, alternator, recuperator, and generator. Waste heat recovery can be used in combined heat and power systems to achieve energy efficiency levels greater than 80 percent. In addition to power generation, microturbines offer an efficient and clean solution to direct mechanical drive markets such as compression and air conditioning.

Microturbines are very fuel price sensitive. At natural gas prices below $2.00/mcf, electricity from microturbines can be produced for around 10 cents/KWh. At prices above $6.00/mcf, generation costs can run in the same range as solar photovoltaics.

Microturbines could run relatively cleanly on hydrogen.

HYDROGEN

There are more than just a few energy visionaries who seem to see the post carbon future- that Future is the <u>Solar Hydrogen Energy System</u>. Hydrogen is the smallest of all atoms. It is the lightest of all gases. When you burn hydrogen, you get water. When you look at the ocean, it's fun, if not educational, to think that some profligate energy culture in the far distant past had enormous reserves of hydrogen that they used at an unprecedented rate creating more and more water pollution. The scientists of the time warned that the continued use of hydrogen would result in the creation of large bodies of water that had heretofore never existed. Alas, the warnings of the scientists went unheeded and they all drowned in their own waste.

We talk about how hydrogen cars create harmless water vapor. Water vapor coming out of the tailpipe of a <u>hydrogen powered</u> car is not harmless if the temperature is 28 degrees. What you have then is a recipe for a car skating rink. A freeway full of cars and trucks belching water vapor could seriously raise the humidity and the temperature. Why, we could drown in all that pure water. So, you see, there are some real issues here.

I find it interesting that almost any conversation about hydrogen starts out with, "but isn't it dangerous?" Yes, hydrogen is explosive. That's kind of the idea when it comes to a fuel. Gasoline explodes. That's the reason the piston in your car drives the crankshaft down. Natural gas explodes. That's the reason a natural gas turbine turns. The propane in your outdoor cooker explodes. And it will settle into your basement. At least hydrogen will not accumulate in low places. After all, it is 8 times lighter than methane. You will never hear of an entire valley blowing up in a hydrogen-based economy. In the Hydrogen Age, the likelihood of the Texas City styled disaster of the petrochemical age is decidedly less. The Hindenberg burned its passengers with the diesel that fell from its tanks, not the hydrogen that kept it afloat.

Hydrogen can be used in any application in which fossil fuels are being used today with the sole exception of cases in which carbon is specifically needed. Hydrogen can be used as a fuel in furnaces, internal combustion engines, turbines and jet engines, even more efficiently than fossil fuels, i.e., coal, petroleum, and natural gas. Automobiles, buses, trains, ships, submarines, airplanes and rockets can run on hydrogen. Hydrogen can also be converted directly to electricity by fuel cells, with a variety of applications in transportation and stationary power generation. Metal hydride technologies offer a variety of applications in refrigeration, air conditioning, hydrogen storage and purification. Combustion of hydrogen with oxygen results in pure steam, which has many applications in industrial processes and space heating. Moreover, hydrogen is an important industrial gas and raw material in numerous industries, such as computer, metallurgical, chemical, pharmaceutical, fertilizer and food industries.

Since hydrogen does not exist in its pure form in nature, hydrogen is not really an energy source-it is an energy carrier. It can be produced from water using electrolysis or high heat. It can be derived from plants and through chemical reformation. It is the energy carrier that can be used to smooth out the intermittent characteristics of renewable energy sources.

Instead of using wires to transport energy from renewable energy rich resource regimes, that energy can be transformed into hydrogen and shipped in pipelines-reconditioned methane pipelines. The results of a study to move energy from the Dakotas to Chicago suggests that a hydrogen pipeline rather than a new high voltage electric transmission line may present greater long-term value.

Another interesting value of a hydrogen pipeline is what occurs at the other end. Not only does a hydrogen pipeline contain energy, it also contains water-very light water. Stripping off the heavy oxygen atom might be the most overall cost-effective way of shipping pure potable water to a water-constricted world. Fortunately for those who would make hydrogen in the deserts from solar energy, the amount of water needed to provide the hydrogen energy is only about 70 gallons per MWh. At the price that you pay for bottled water in the convenience store, there is still more value in the water than in the energy.

The Hydrogen industry is a mature industry. Hydrogen as a product has been provided for industry for various processes for decades by companies that specialize in its production and handling. There is also a market for oxygen. Up to now, there has not been a mass market to drive the costs down or the processes to their technological bests.

One such "Hydrogen" company is Stuart Energy:

Stuart Energy has a proud, 54-year history as a pioneering organization in hydrogen technology research, development and product engineering. The vision for distributed, on-site creation of hydrogen through water electrolysis began with Alexander T. Stuart in 1905, and began to be commercially realized when he and his son, Alexander K. (Sandy) Stuart, the current chairman, formed the Company in 1948. Today, the Stuart Energy vision is one of the industry's driving forces that is ushering in the new hydrogen economy. As a result, we are strongly positioned with a first-mover advantage in the rapidly expanding hydrogen marketplace. We are in a race to become the global leader in building the infrastructure for the emerging hydrogen economy and we are focused on our strategic goal of meeting the world's growing demand for hydrogen as a safe, clean, secure and sustainable source of energy.

Stuart is now offering most of the technologies required to move towards the goal of an advanced solar-hydrogen economy. Efficiencies of water to hydrogen to energy are running in the high 70s.

There are numerous other companies working on storage technologies. One such technology is the Powerball concept. Another technology under development is the Millennium Cell.

There is a recent paper published on hydrogen, which concludes that the Hydrogen economy will be too inefficient and the energy carrier of choice should be methanol. The paper fails to mention that methanol is poison. The authors' arguments are not without merit however and their recommendation to find "technical solutions for a sustainable energy future characterized by two closed natural cycles of water and CO2 or hydrogen and carbon is a good one.

However, in the big picture, the simplicity and universality of a hydrogen economy is more than appealing. The issue of efficiency is important, but we are not talking about a finite resource here. If a large 5-megawatt wind turbine can produce electricity for 2 cents/KWh and the hydrogen energy it produces can be shipped for a fraction of that to a fuel cell or turbine which is 90 % efficient, who cares if the electrolysis process is only 80 % efficient? If the built environment is composed of nanoconducting PV paints that produce electricity at 1 cent/KWh, who cares if hydrogen carries 1/3 the energy per unit of volume of methane? The total cost of the KWh is still substantially less than the current cost and there is no pollution or depletion.

The same hydrogen can be used to power our cars, our homes, our stoves, our jetliners, and our ocean liners. There would be no such thing as an oil spill or a beach cleanup from a tanker that has been driven off course by the ever-increasing amount of tropical storms.

The marriage of hydrogen and electricity will provide Earth with an energy system that is clean, sustainable, and equitable.

"Truth is a fruit which should not be plucked until it is ripe."

Voltaire

Chapter Six

A Stitch *in* Time

The Plan

"Be braver—you can't cross a chasm in two small jumps."

David Lloyd George

It all seems so straightforward.

There seems to be little doubt. The carbon age is going to end and it may start its decline sooner than many of us think. If oil production peaks in the next few years, gasoline prices will be higher and the cost of commuting and practically everything else will go up. Natural gas, although seemingly plentiful, may follow right behind. Of course, with over 75% of known oil reserves in the hands of Islamic countries, anything can and probably will happen. Most of the world's gas reserves are in the old Soviet Union.

In a way, tightened energy stocks could be a good thing. Higher gasoline prices would make commuting more expensive which would arguably slow down the decline in air quality in Austin. It would have an effect on urban sprawl. It might encourage a denser, more compact city with real neighborhoods and transportation options other than the car. Higher oil prices would probably leak over into higher natural gas prices. That would make electricity and heating more expensive. That too, could be a good thing, because Austin Energy's conservation programs and energy efficiency programs would be more in demand and more successful. If the price of gas went up by more than a few dollars per mcf, the green pricing program at Austin Energy would look pretty good considering that the green rate replaces the fuel charge. It would therefore protect those farsighted subscribers from skyrocketing fuel charges. That would be a good thing.

And it is a good thing that renewable and sustainable technologies have made such strides in development in the last 20 years. It is truly amazing and encouraging that the long-term price for a wind generated KWh to a Texas utility is probably less than that utility's average marginal cost of producing a KWh. Wind power is cheap. Conservation and efficiency is cheap. Solar hot water is competitive. Fuel cells are coming. Zero energy homes and buildings can make sense now. Energy from our waste dumps is competitive now. Solar plants built on the bulk scale can compete with nuclear and coal if we make it a priority.

But let's not kid ourselves. The change in climate that is predicted for Central Texas is a bad thing. Summers will be hotter, rivers will be dryer, lakes will be lower, and English lawns will seem more and more ridiculous. Air conditioning bills will go up, heating bills will go down. Rain, when it comes, will likely come harder and faster. That will mean more and more floods with greater impact on the built environment as those floodwaters careen through it. Air quality will continue to be an area of concern for health officials. There will be more diseases from the tropics and there will be increased morbidity in the old and infirmed from heat storms.

True, as a city of one million, we cannot stop climate change and its effects. But we can prepare for the regulatory environment that will come once the need to control the amount of carbon that we presently put into the environment is no longer a respectable debate and is instead a question of equitable enforcement. We should begin now to prepare ourselves for climate change by changing our lawns to low water use gardens. We can begin now to make our homes and businesses as efficient as possible. That would be a good thing.

And we can control the quality of our air. Yes, there is a lot of pollution that comes from Houston and the other polluted skies of Texas, but most of our ozone problem comes from our own car and truck fleets. Air quality will get much better if nonpolluting fuels and electricity power a substantial portion of those fleets.

But mostly, it is a bad thing to think that we cannot do something great. It is a bad thing to think that pollution, resource depletion, and the capital exportation required to bring in those resources is just the way it has to be.

Because, you see, it doesn't have to be that way.

We can have a bustling, dynamic city without resource depletion or pollution, but we must have the vision to want it and the wisdom and perseverance to see that it is done.

If you are of the age to remember things that happened forty years ago, you probably remember when President Kennedy made his speech to Congress about going to the moon. He proposed that this nation do something great:

Special Message to the Congress on Urgent National Needs
President John F. Kennedy
delivered in person before a joint session of Congress,
May 25, 1961.

"Finally, if we are to win the battle that is now going on around the world between freedom and tyranny, the dramatic achievements in space which occurred in recent weeks should have made clear to us all, as did the Sputnik in 1957, the impact of this adventure on the minds of men everywhere, who are attempting to make a determination of which road they should take. Since early in my term, our efforts in space have been under review. With the advice of the Vice President, who is Chairman of the National Space Council, we have examined where we are strong and where we are not, where we may succeed and where we may not. Now it is time to take longer strides—time for a great new American enterprise—time for this nation to take a clearly leading role in space achievement, which in many ways may hold the key to our future on earth.

I believe we possess all the resources and talents necessary. But the facts of the matter are that we have never made the national decisions or marshaled the national resources required for such leadership. We have never specified long-range goals on an urgent time schedule, or managed our resources and our time so as to insure their fulfillment.

Recognizing the head start obtained by the Soviets with their large rocket engines, which gives them many months of lead-time, and recognizing the likelihood that they will exploit this lead for some time to come in still more impressive successes, we nevertheless are required to make new efforts on our own. For while we cannot guarantee that we shall one day be first, we can guarantee that any failure to make this effort will make us last. We take an additional risk by making it in full view of the world, but as shown by the feat of astronaut Shepard, this very risk enhances our stature when we are successful. But this is not merely a race. Space is open to us now; and our eagerness to share its meaning is not governed by the efforts of others. We go into space because whatever mankind must undertake, free men must fully share.

I therefore ask the Congress, above and beyond the increases I have earlier requested for space activities, to provide the funds which are needed to meet the following national goals:

First, I believe that this nation should commit itself to achieving the goal, before this decade is out, of landing a man on the moon and returning him safely to the earth. No single space project in this period will be more impressive to mankind, or more important for the long-range exploration of space; and none will be so difficult or expensive to accomplish. We propose to accelerate the development of the appropriate lunar spacecraft. We propose to develop alternate liquid and solid fuel boosters, much larger than any now being developed, until certain which is superior. We propose additional funds for other engine development and for unmanned explorations—explorations which are particularly important for one purpose which this nation will never overlook: the survival of the man who first makes this daring flight. But in a very real sense, it will not be one man going to the moon—if we make this judgment affirmatively, it will be an entire nation. For all of us must work to put him there."

President Kennedy addressed Rice University roughly 9 months later. Here are some portions of his comments:

"No man can fully grasp how far and how fast we have come, but condense, if you will, the 50,000 years of man's recorded history in a time span of but a half century. Stated in these terms, we know very little about the first 40 years, except at the end of them advanced man had learned to use the skins of animals to cover them. Then about two years ago, under this standard, man emerged from his caves to construct other kinds of shelter. Only 5 years ago man learned to write and use a cart with wheels. Christianity began less than 2 years ago. The printing press came this year, and then less than 2 months ago, during this whole 50-year span of human history, the steam engine provided a new source of power.

Newton explored the meaning of gravity. Last month electric lights and telephones and automobiles and airplanes became available. Only last week did we develop penicillin and television and nuclear power, and now if America's new spacecraft succeeds in reaching Venus, we will have literally reached the stars before midnight tonight.

This is a breathtaking pace, and such a pace cannot help but create new ills as it dispels old, new ignorance, new problems, new dangers. Surely the opening vistas of space promise high costs and hardships, as well as high reward.

So it is not surprising that some would have us stay where we are a little longer to rest, to wait. But this city of Houston, this State of Texas, this country of the United States was not built by those who waited and rested and wished to look behind them. This country was conquered by those who moved forward-and so will space.

William Bradford, speaking in 1630 of the founding of the Plymouth Bay Colony, said that all great and honorable actions are accompanied with great difficulties, and both must be enterprised and overcome with answerable courage.

If this capsule history of our progress teaches us anything, it is that man, in his quest for knowledge and progress, is determined and cannot be deterred. The exploration of space will go ahead, whether we join in it or not, and it is one of the great adventures of all time, and no nation which expects to be the leader of other nations can expect to stay behind in this race for space.

Those who came before us made certain that this country rode the first waves of the industrial revolutions, the first waves of modern invention, and the first wave of nuclear power, and this generation does not intend to founder in the backwash of the coming age of space. We mean to be a part of it-we mean to lead it. For the eyes of the world now look into space, to the moon and to the planets beyond, and we have vowed that we shall not see it governed by a hostile flag of conquest, but by a banner of freedom and peace. We have vowed that we shall not see space filled with weapons of mass destruction, but with instruments of knowledge and understanding.

Yet the vows of this Nation can only be fulfilled if we in this Nation are first, and, therefore, we intend to be first. In short, our leadership in science and in industry, our hopes for peace and security, our obligations to ourselves as well as others, all require us to make this effort, to solve these mysteries, to solve them for the good of all men, and to become the world's leading space-faring nation.

We set sail on this new sea because there is new knowledge to be gained, and new rights to be won, and they must be won and used for the progress of all people. For space science, like nuclear science and all technology, has no conscience of its own.

Whether it will become a force for good or ill depends on man, and only if the United States occupies a position of pre-eminence can we help decide whether this new ocean will be a sea of peace or a new terrifying theater of war. I do not say that we should or will go unprotected against the hostile misuse of space any more than we go unprotected against the hostile use of land or sea, but I do say that space can be explored and mastered without feeding the fires of war, without repeating the mistakes that man has made in extending his writ around this globe of ours.

We choose to go to the moon. We choose to go to the moon in this decade and do the other things, not because they are easy, but because they are hard, because that goal will serve to organize and measure the best of our energies and skills, because that challenge is one that we are willing to accept, one we are unwilling to postpone, and one which we intend to win, and the others, too."

Eight years later on August 16, 1969, two Americans were taking their first steps on the moon. It was a colossal achievement and one that the World will long remember in textbooks and cultural lore.

Could we, the City of Austin, with our neighbors and allies, with the help of the Department of Energy and the State Energy Office, embark upon our own project of vision that would bring the Sun and Sustainability to Austin?

Just as the island nation of Iceland has decided, could we choose to begin to create a sustainable hydrogen based economy and "do the other things, not because they are easy, but because they are hard, because that goal will serve to organize and measure the best of our energies and skills, because that challenge is one that we are willing to accept, one we are unwilling to postpone, and one which we intend to win?"

Dealing with the challenges of climate change and the end of the carbon age deserves the best of our energies. "We set sail on this new sea because there is new knowledge to be gained, and new rights to be won, and they must be won and used for the progress of all people." For Sun science, like all science and all technology, has no conscience of its own.

Our leadership in science and in industry, our hopes for prosperity, our obligations to ourselves as well as those generations that follow us require us to make this effort, to meet these challenges, to solve them for the good of all men, and to become the world's leading Sun-faring City.

Can we choose to do this?

Of course we can!

We chose to build a nuclear plant. We chose to build the dams that created the Highland Lakes. We can choose to be the most livable city anywhere.

To bring the Sun, we must have a plan. Like the plan that took mankind to the Moon forty years ago, we must distil thousands of decisions and goals into discrete programs, not unlike the Mercury Program, the Gemini Program, and the Apollo Program.

We must identify or develop what we need, confirm that it will work, and deploy our findings and developments effectively and economically. These stages will be known as Project Matrix, The Probus Program, and Actus. Each program will consider the transportation sector, the building sector, and the electric sector. In many cases, these sectors will necessarily overlap. The unification of the transportation and electric sectors is an obvious example. Zero energy buildings will involve both buildings and electric. Land use planning will involve all three of these areas. Mass transportation will necessarily involve land use planning, buildings, transportation, and electric.

PROJECT MATRIX

Project Matrix is the formal process of identifying and assessing what we will need in order to move Austin and Austin Energy into the actualization stage of becoming a sustainable city. It will create the matrix of issues, strategies, technologies, and philosophy that must be considered in order to implement a long term comprehensive energy plan that reduces the undesirable environmental, social, and economic impacts of energy use.

The City of Austin states in its own commitment to its citizens: We want to be the most livable community in the country.

The current VISION of Austin Energy is "Austin Energy will be an exceptional community-owned utility through our relentless commitment to our customers and our community."

The current MISSION states that "Austin Energy provides extraordinary customer service, affordable and reliable energy, environmental leadership and exceptional value for our community."

WHAT WE NEED

To SUCCEED we will need the following:

We will need a strong endorsement by the Citizens of Austin.

We will need a Council and a Mayor willing and capable of implementing that endorsement.

We must have an Austin Energy willing to follow through and redefine itself along the lines of its existing mission statement and a new vision which maximizes the potential of Austin Energy.

We will need to receive the full cooperation from all the relevant departments of the federal government and the state government.

We will need the cooperation of our neighboring cities, the county, and the surrounding counties.

We will need the cooperation of the business community and the educational community.

THE ELECTRIC SECTOR

Austin Energy is the key and the door to obtaining the vision of a truly sustainable city. Austin Energy and its management will have to whole-heartedly embrace this task. It will need to grow a new skin and leave the old one behind. Management will need to craft a new vision statement that captures the potential of Austin Energy and the imagination of the Citizens of Austin. It will need to craft a vision statement that redefines Austin Energy as a provider of energy and service. That energy might come as cooling, or heat, communication services, or even transportation. In order to become a leader in the protection of the environment, our vision must include the development of the sustainable technologies that will be required to provide that protection.

Nowhere in the existing Vision or Mission statements is the word electricity used. We think we sell KWhs. Indeed, that is what we have been selling for more than 100 years. But, in the end, we are actually selling comfort and convenience to our customer stockholders. The existing Vision states that "Austin Energy will be an exceptional community-owned utility through our relentless commitment to our customers and our community." As a community owned utility, we owe it to the community to actualize our full potential.

To accomplish our goal, we must have a plan to meet our growth and we must have a plan to replace our existing generation with sustainable alternatives. To become a sustainable city, we should look at all of our plants and plans- past, present, and future, with an eye for how they will fit into a vision of sustainability and a future solar-hydrogen economy. At present growth rates, it can be imagined that our generation needs will double in the next twenty-five years. In order to have a sustainable utility and city, we must build 2500 new megawatts and convert the existing 2500 megawatts in the same time frame.

NEW GENERATION

To meet the needs of AE's growth sustainably, a combination of new bulk power plants, distributed generation, and future unification with the transportation sector will be employed. Resources will come from the sun, the wind, biomass, geothermal, and other forms of renewable energy. Hydrogen and electricity will be the energy carriers that unify the system. Advanced emerging technologies should be considered.

New Generation Need Number One

Determine the cost and strategy and percent of new growth that can be met with Zero Energy Buildings. Explore potential of AE expansion into PV industry.

New Generation Need Number Two

Determine the costs and percent of new growth that can be met with wind power. Also determine the cost and most economic method of transmission of wind energy. Explore the potential of AE joint venture agreements with wind energy generators.

New Generation Need Number Three

Assess the cost and most economic bulk power technologies for solar generated electricity and the most economic method of transmission from resource regimes. Explore the potential of AE development of bulk solar plants for resale or joint ventures with other generators.

New Generation Need Number Four

Assess the potential and percent of new growth that can be met through unification of transportation sector with the electric sector and the peak shaving potential that may be achieved.

New Generation Need Number Five

Determine the cost and percent of new load that can be met through reversible hydrogen fuel cells. Assess the development of bi-directional cells and their capability to store energy off peak and deliver energy on peak. Explore the potential of AE expansion into industry through joint ventures and strategic alliances.

New Generation Need Number Six

Determine the cost and percent of load that can be met with geothermal heat pumps and ultra high efficiency air conditioning. Assess the potential of solar thermal air-conditioning.

New Generation Need Number Seven

Determine the percent of new load that can be met through high tech conservation and efficiency methods.

New Generation Need Number Eight

Determine the potential of micro-turbines and assess AE expansion into the industry through strategic alliances.

New Generation Need Number Nine

Determine the cost and potential of storage technologies at the regional, local, and distributed levels. Assessment would include large-scale storage of wind and solar energy, medium scale storage for neighborhoods, and small-scale storage through reversible fuel cell technologies.

New Generation Need Number Ten

Determine the cost of large-scale hydrogen production at the point of resource conversion and the cost of the transportation of hydrogen using existing pipelines or right of ways. Assess the value of the water as a co-product of the hydrogen energy stream.

CONVERSION OF EXISTING GENERATION

In order to make existing generation sustainable, the existing carbon and nuclear fleet must be converted to sustainable fuels or they must be decommissioned. The most likely and most potentially available sustainable fuel for the gas plants is hydrogen. The coal plant could be converted to a biomass / hydrogen hybrid conversion that would possibly reemploy the existing assets to their optimal capability.

Project	Installation Dates	Net Capacity
Holly (gas/oil) - 4 units	1960-74	570 MW
Decker (gas/oil) - 2 units	1970-77	770 MW
Fayette (coal) - 2 units	1979-80	600 MW
Decker (gas turbine) - 4 units	1988	200 MW
South Texas Project (Nuclear) - 2 units	1988-89	400 MW
Renewables (wind/landfill/solar)	1986-2001	101 MW
Sand Hill (gas)	2001	180 MW
	2004	300 MW
Total		3,121 MW
System Peak Demand:		2,383 MW

Existing Electric Need Number One

Determine cost and future equipment availability for hydrogen conversion of existing gas plants.

Existing Electric Need Number Two

Determine cost and future feasibility of biomass conversion of coal plant.

Existing Electric Need Number Three

Determine cost of decommissioning nuclear plant and assess conversion to alternative generation or other use.

Existing Electric Need Number Four

Determine cost and equipment availability for the conversion of existing natural gas pipelines to hydrogen pipelines.

Existing Electric Need Number Five

Determine if hydrogen fuel cells on a neighborhood scale can be integrated more economically than conversion of existing carbon generation fleet.

Existing Electric Need Number Six

Determine if a combination of fuel cells, solar, and other DG can be integrated more economically than conversion of existing carbon fleet.

Existing Electric Need Number Seven

Determine what pieces of the existing carbon fleet can be more valuable in alternative use scenarios.

Existing Electric Need Number Eight

Determine what percent of existing generation can be replaced by efficiency and conservation and at what cost.

Existing Electric Need Number Nine

Assess the potential for advanced emerging energy systems including the potential of the unification of the transportation sector with the electric sector.

Existing Electric Need Number Ten

Establish a realistic timetable for a transition process and estimate total conversion cost for the most economical strategy.

NEW BUSINESS CONCEPT

Austin Energy is one of the largest businesses in Austin. AE ranks among the top twenty in corporate employers and fourth in gross revenues among locally publicly traded companies. But make no mistake about it, Austin Energy collects more income from Austin residents and businesses than any other company period. Austin Energy could and should become a community energy company that provides much more than just KWhs. A revised business model would require Austin Energy to assess other business and service opportunities. Austin Energy has the potential to become a great energy company that leads the world in the development of sustainable energy. Such a company could not only maintain the current large transfers to the city government, it could provide much larger transfers if it was allowed to compete and grow as a world leader in sustainable energy development.

With Austin as its base, Austin Energy, like any other major energy company, could grow to provide sustainable energy services and electricity in other markets around the world. Not unlike the way that the Green Building Program has become to be recognized as a knowledgeable and marketable commodity, Austin Energy could become a leader in solar cell manufacturing, reversible fuel cells, micro-turbines, zero energy structures, hydrogen production and transmission, and fossil fuel plant re-powering. With proper management and vision, transfers to the general fund could increase and rates could even be reduced.

New Business Concept One

Determine what statutory and bonding authority restrictions would be or might be problematic in expanding the scope of the Austin Energy market and its marketable commodities, technologies, and expertise.

New Business Concept Two

Craft a new business entity that can compete and grow in the world energy markets if it is determined that such statutory or bonding restrictions do exist.

New Business Concept Three

Consider the potential of formal strategic alliances with other public power entities in the region and the potential for the creation of a community energy company that can compete effectively on a global scale.

New Business Concept Four

Determine if the current governance of Austin Energy can be reshaped to allow the maximum potential of Austin Energy to be actualized.

New Business Concept Five

Determine the political and civic implications and assess the potential of Austin Energy expanding into the transportation and building sectors.

THE TRANSPORTATION SECTOR

Although only a third of our total emissions come from the transportation sector with the balance coming from our power plants, the transportation sector is responsible for more than 2/3 of the emissions that help to make smog. And smog is bad for the health of everyone. The American Lung Association constantly reminds us, and our regulators, of this important truth. Smog kills.

Austinites drive about 20 million miles a day. I don't know why.

The truth is, we drive because we can. We drive because we can afford it. Or at least we believe we can afford it. I DON'T think about smog, or of lung disease, about leaving the most expensive resources for my grandchildren, of the oil wars in the Mideast, polluting the aquifer, or changing climate when I jump in my Chevy and drive to work.

I wish that I did not live in a city dominated by the car. But I do.

The car-dominated cities of the developed world have somewhat institutionalized themselves. The system of freeways and roads that have developed since the Second World War make walking in many of our post war neighborhoods unsavory to say the least. In some ways, it is dangerous, and to some law enforcement officials, it is suspicious. Try walking along Mopac or even crossing Mopac. You will find yourself feeling like one of those people with a cardboard sign in their hand.

Seventy years ago when General Motors bought the light rail system in Los Angeles and then promptly tore it up, it was following a brilliant and pervasive marketing plan. Every grown-up American needs a car. And every house should have a two and

150

now a three-car garage attached to it with an electric garage door opener.

What we have done to our cities is analogous to what the ox cart did to the old cities in Europe. Roads for animal-powered carts or carriages can be narrow. The built environment that grew up around those roads made it almost impossible for a car to navigate within it. Now those areas of the older cities are the most pedestrian dominated.

And they have the most charm. People feel a better sense of place when they do not have to share it with tens if not hundreds of 4,000-pound metal servants.

What will happen to our car-dominated cities in 200 years? And how do we make the most of our car-dominated built environment?

Since we do have the infrastructure for almost everyone to have a car or personal transportation device, it seems we should strive to make the personal transportation device as useful as possible. To achieve this optimization of allocation of resources, this PTD should be seamlessly integrated into the overall system of energy infrastructure.

THE UNIFIED ENERGY SYSTEM

There is entirely too much waste and inefficiency in our present system which separates the potential in our transportation sector from the potential in our electric sector. According to Travis County records, there are more cars registered in Travis County than there are people. A million cars with an average of 100-horsepower each is the equivalent of 100 coal plants worth of power capacity. Not one horsepower of it is used to reduce our investment in electric generation capacity.

Clearly, there is some room for improvement here.

Even our current fleet of buses can in no way be integrated into an overall energy system.

To blend these two systems together, we must make an interface. And that interface will need to be electric. Electric cars with batteries, hybrid vehicles with electric interface potential, buses with ultra-capacitors, ultra-light elevated monorail PTDs, electric scooters and bikes, and Segways will all accomplish this unification. More diesel buses and non-electric light rail will not.

Theoretically, a PTD could be the power source for your house. Theoretically, a lot of PTDs could power the work place. Stadiums and auditoriums could be powered by the PTDs of the crowds that attend them.

It's no different from using your horse to travel into town in the morning then using him to pull the plow that will plant the seeds in your field in the afternoon.

Transportation Sector Need Number One

Determine and assess the potential for generation capacity from the transportation sector.

Transportation Sector Need Number Two

Assess the potential of developing strategic alliances to develop and provide PTDs that can be integrated into the electric generation infrastructure.

Transportation Sector Need Number Three

Determine the nature and costs of an extensive public interface of the transportation sector with the electric generation system.

Transportation Sector Need Number Four

Assess the income potential of AE expansion into the Transportation sector.

Transportation Sector Need Number Five

Assess the economic development potential of the PTD industry to Austin and surrounding areas.

Transportation Sector Need Number Six

Explore the potential of a public transportation and PTD system interface.

Transportation Sector Need Number Seven

Assess the potential of widespread telework programs and explore how to enhance the telework workplace through the creation of virtual as well as actual workplace environments.

Transportation Sector Need Number Eight

Assess the potential of widespread ride and car sharing.

Transportation Sector Need Number Nine

Assess the public appeal of an elevated public transportation system.

Transportation Sector Need Number Ten

Design and determine the costs of an extensive system of sidewalks and right of ways for human-powered vehicles, small PTDs, and pedestrians.

BUILDINGS

I can't help it. I confess. Whenever I come into Austin, I look at the buildings and think, "that's my town." I know that a town is its people. But when I come in to Austin from the north, I always take the elevated section so I can see The University, the Capitol, and Downtown. It somehow gives me pleasure. It must work for a lot of people. Otherwise, why would the Networks pay for somebody's blimp to hover around taking pictures of the downtown skyline of the city of the event they are covering?

I like skylines. Somehow they speak of our accomplishments and of our wealth and power over our natural environment. It's the same feeling as mowing your lawn only much bigger. And even though many skylines make for a terrible place to be on a weekend, (New York is a big exception) we somehow identify with them and think of them as our home, or our castle. And when some outside force changes that skyline? Well, to quote Merle Haggard, "you're walking on the fighting side of me."

In some other galaxy far away, each person might carry extensive portable homes that spring out of their backs, much like the people in this galaxy who quote, "go camping."

People could carry their house around I guess. Turtles seem to do OK. They are, after all, the metaphorical basis of a rather interesting and often neglected childhood story. Snails seem to thrive OK, but they are too slow. Gypsies are not generally well regarded, but Snow Birds, on the other hand, on their way to South Texas are regarded positively if not curiously.

My house in Mexico has walls that are about two feet thick. They are made of stone. The windows and door openings are more like passageways. When I come back to the so-called developed world, I often feel like many of the structures that I visit are made out of cardboard. Some are. A million dollar house in West Austin with 6-inch walls feels like an imposter to me. In many ways, I would rather be in a high tech tension structure covered with a nanofiber that produces electricity, reflects and conducts heat and light, yet cannot be cut with a chain saw. Maybe some day I will be able to realize that desire.

In the meantime, we all live and work in the built environment that exists today. And it exists because that's the way it was done. In Spanish, there is a saying, "Así es, como es." It is as it is.

THE BUILT ENVIRONMENT

We can actually do a lot with our structures. We can retrofit with new lighting. We can replace that dark composite shingle roof with a white reflective roof. If we really want to spend some money, we can change out the windows. We can blow more insulation in the attic. We can test and repair our ductwork. We can shade the windows on the west from the sun with trees or with window shades. We can coat the outside with a super reflective paint that is harder than a ceramic.

We can ventilate the attic or spray water on the roof. We can grow vines on the walls and on a trellis that covers the roof. We can employ smart lights, smart thermostats, smart window coverings, and smart glass. We can change our light bulbs and our showerheads.

We can wear white short sleeve clothes in the summer and dark sweaters in the winter.

Most of the energy we use in our homes in Central Texas goes to keeping us cool in the summer. With climate change this will only get worse. True, a hot room is in a higher state of energy than a cool room. Why we have to use energy to take a room from a higher state of energy to a lower state seems a little crude, but then again, humankind invented air conditioning just 50 years ago.

Given that AE has such a history of building efficiency through its conservation and green building programs, most of the needs in the building sector are beyond Matrix and are in the Probus or Actus stage of development

Built Environment Need Number One

Assess the total amount of efficiency available in the residential and commercial sectors at varied levels of capital outlays using various efficiency programs.

Built Environment Need Number Two

Determine how Austin Energy might further increase its revenue stream through an expansion into those markets.

Built Environment Need Number Three

Determine and assess the potential of aggressive programs designed to provide chilled water and off-peak storage for the commercial and industrial sectors.

Built Environment Need Number Four

Determine and assess the total potential of the built environment for solar access. (Including parking lots and garages)

FUTURE BUILDINGS

A well-designed building with today's advanced designs and technology should be able to heat, cool, and power itself without outside inputs. These buildings are the future.

Future Building Need Number One

Through the Green Building Program, determine and/or develop with strategic partner a cost-effective reflective roofing system with integrated PV generation.

Future Building Need Number Two

Develop through Green Building a zero net energy or 120 house or structure design program to meet future growth in the residential and commercial sectors.

Future Building Need Number Three

Promote and develop Smart House Technology.

Future Building Need Number Four

Promote and develop Integrated Structural PV Power Glazings for commercial high-rise structures.

Future Building Need Number Five

Determine the potential of co-powering structures through a symbiosis of PTDs, and DG.

PROBUS

The Matrix Project will establish the environment and structure to initiate the processes that will provide the parameters, data, and direction for PROBUS. As each element in the Matrix is developed, each segment of that completed MATRIX is moved to PROBUS to pursue funding and initiate testing in the real environments of technological development, customer acceptance, and resource availability.

THE ELECTRIC SECTOR

NEW GENERATION

New Generation Need Number One

Determine the cost and strategy and percent of new growth that can be met with Zero Energy Buildings. Explore potential of AE expansion into PV industry.

Probus 11.1

Initiate program through Green Building in conjunction with builder groups to test technology and marketability of Zero Energy Housing. Consider concept of purchasing the home with "all bills paid". Work with Commercial Developer to develop commercial zero energy profiles.

New Generation Need Number Two

Determine the costs and percent of new growth that can be met with wind power. Also determine the cost and most economic method of transmission of wind energy. Explore the potential of AE joint venture agreements with wind energy generators.

Probus 12.1

Work with Industry groups to determine potential of wind power considering transmission restraints and resource characteristics. Determine time and availability of resources for different resource regimes.

New Generation Need Number Three

Assess the cost and most economic bulk power technologies for solar generated electricity and the most economic method of transmission from resource regimes. Explore the potential of AE development of bulk solar plants for resale or joint ventures with other generators.

Probus 13.1

Rank and assess through COF Tech Committee the most promising technologies for solar generation. Work with Industry, Government labs, and local incubator.

Work with ERCOT to determine best transmission tracks to transmit solar energy from resource regimes. Consider strategic partnerships with owners of promising technologies.

New Generation Need Number Four

Assess the potential and percent of new growth that can be met through unification of transportation sector with the electric sector and the peak shaving potential that may be achieved.

Probus 14.1

Through COF Tech Committee, initiate potential of strategic partnerships with transportation sector and determine cost and feasibility of unification of the two sectors. RFP is developed.

New Generation Need Number Five

Determine the cost and percent of new load that can be met through reversible hydrogen fuel cells. Assess the development of bi-directional cells and their capability to store energy off peak and deliver energy on peak. Explore the potential of AE expansion into industry through joint ventures and strategic alliances.

Probus 15.1

Expand present fuel cell program to include bi-directional

reversible fuel cells. Identify companies that are currently offering electrolysis equipment. Through COF Tech Committee, initiate preliminary negotiations for joint venture or strategic alliance. (RFP)

New Generation Need Number Six

Determine the cost and percent of load that can be met with geothermal heat pumps and ultra high efficiency air conditioning.

Probus 16.1

Work with Industry Groups and DOE Office of Energy Efficiency to estimate potential of resource and technological advancement potential.

New Generation Need Number Seven

Determine the percent of new load that can be met through high tech conservation and efficiency methods.

Probus 17.1

Work with Industry Groups and DOE Office of Energy Efficiency to estimate potential of resource and technological advancement potential. Develop RFP.

New Generation Need Number Eight

Determine the potential of micro-turbines and assess AE expansion into the industry through strategic alliances.

Probus 18.1

Work with Industry Groups and DOE to estimate potential and costs of resource and technological advancement potential. Develop RFP

New Generation Need Number Nine

Determine the cost and potential of storage technologies at the regional, local, and distributed levels. Assessment would include large-scale storage of wind and solar energy, medium scale storage for neighborhoods, and small-scale storage through reversible fuel cell technologies, flywheels, and other technologies. Develop RFP

Probus 19.1

Through COF Tech Committee, work with developers of compressed air storage, flywheel storage, reversible fuel cell storage, and other energy storage labs and associations and commit to testing leading candidates at each level. (RFP)

New Generation Need Number Ten

Determine the cost of large-scale hydrogen production at the point of resource conversion and the cost of the transportation of hydrogen using existing pipelines or rights of way. Assess the value of the water as a co-product of the hydrogen energy stream.

Probus 20.1

Work with Industry groups and National Labs through COF Tech Committee to test a section of existing pipeline and set up a demonstration project of hydrogen production. (RFP)

EXISTING GENERATION

Existing Electric Need Number One

Determine cost and future equipment availability for hydrogen conversion of existing gas plants.

Probus 1.1

Develop and participate in DOE, multi-state, multi-utility project to test hydrogen turbines and hydrogen combined cycle. (RFP)

Existing Electric Need Number Two

Determine cost and future feasibility of biomass conversion of coal plant.

Probus 2.1

Develop and participate in DOE, multi-state, multi-utility project to develop biomass turbines or boilers for coal conversions. (RFP)

Existing Electric Need Number Three

Determine cost of decommissioning nuclear plant and conversion of site to alternative generation or use.

Probus 3.1

In concert with partners in STNP, initiate request to DOE and NRC to consider alternative scenarios for South Texas Nuclear Plant. Consider selling asset in near term.

Existing Electric Need Number Four

Determine cost and equipment availability for the conversion of existing natural gas pipelines to hydrogen pipelines.

Probus 4.1

Develop strategic partnerships with hydrogen and gas utilities and develop and participate in test conversion of existing pipelines and determine methodology for new hydrogen pipelines. Work on RFP with DOE

Existing Electric Need Number Five

Determine if hydrogen fuel cells on a neighborhood scale can be integrated more economically than conversion of existing carbon generation fleet.

Probus 5.1

Continue to monitor and expand present fuel cell program.

Existing Electric Need Number Six

Determine if combination of fuel cells, solar, and other DG can be integrated more economically than conversion of existing carbon fleet. (RFP)

Probus 6.1

Continue to monitor and expand present photovoltaic experience using various technologies and strategies. Initiate a microturbine program at varying scale.

Existing Electric Need Number Seven

Determine what pieces of the existing carbon fleet can be more valuable in alternative use scenarios.

Probus 7.1

Initiate dialogue with professionals in the real estate community regarding best use value and timing of value for asset conversions.

Existing Electric Need Number Eight

Determine what percent of existing generation can be replaced by efficiency and conservation and at what cost.

Probus 8.1

Initiate super efficiency test program on a portfolio of existing homes and offices to determine the potential and costs to convert existing built environment. (RFP)

Existing Electric Need Number Nine

Assess the potential for advanced emerging energy systems including the potential of the unification of the transportation sector with the electric sector. (RFP)

Probus 9.1

Develop and participate in test program with DOE, Transportation, and Automotive Industry to develop a prototype PTD that provides storage, generation, and transportation.

Existing Electric Need Number Ten

Establish a realistic timetable for a transition process and estimate total conversion costs for the most economical strategy.

Probus 10.1

Establish a COF Conversion Team. Team would consist of members from RMC, EUC, and COFCOA. COFC Team would have a Tech Committee and Industry Committee.

NEW BUSINESS CONCEPT

New Business Concept One

Determine what statutory and bonding authority restrictions would be or might be problematic in expanding the scope of the Austin Energy market and its marketable commodities, technologies, and expertise.

Probus 21.1

Establish AENB Group consisting of AE Legal, City Manager, and Finance.

New Business Concept Two

Craft a new business entity that can compete and grow in the world energy markets if it is determined that such statutory or bonding restrictions do exist.

Probus 22.1

Establish an AENB Development Group consisting of AENB and COFCOA

New Business Concept Three

Consider the potential of formal strategic alliances with other public power entities in the region and the potential for the creation of a community energy company that can compete effectively on a global scale.

Probus 23.1

Through AENB Development Group, initiate preliminary talks with CPS and LCRA to explore alliance and architecture of such an alliance.

New Business Concept Four

Determine if the current governance of Austin Energy can be reshaped to allow the maximum potential of Austin Energy to be actualized.

Probus 24.1

Create AENB Governance Team consisting of AENB, led by AE VP of Government Affairs.

New Business Concept Five

Determine the political and civic implications and assess the potential of Austin Energy expanding into the transportation and building sectors.

Probus 25.1

Establish COF Civic Group consisting of RMC, EUD, Council, COFCOA, AENB, and COF Tech Committee.

THE TRANSPORTATION SECTOR

Transportation Sector Need Number One

Determine and assess the potential for generation capacity from the transportation sector.

Probus 31.1

COF Tech Committee creates transportation group to initiate exploratory talks with Department of Transportation to develop RFP with DOE.

Transportation Sector Need Number Two

Assess the potential of developing strategic alliances to develop and provide PTDs that can be integrated into the electric generation infrastructure.

Probus 32.1

COF Transportation Group initiates exploratory talks to develop prototype PTD with support from Industry, DOE, DOT, and other stakeholders. Alliances with other cities and regional government are actively pursued and consummated.

Transportation Sector Need Number Three

Determine the nature and costs of an extensive public interface of the transportation sector with the electric generation system.

Probus 33.1

COF Transportation Group initiates study with DOE, DOT, and SECO. RFP needed

Transportation Sector Need Number Four

Assess the income potential of AE expansion into the Transportation sector.

Probus 34.1

Same as 33.1

Transportation Sector Need Number Five

Assess the economic development potential of the PTD industry to Austin and surrounding areas.

Probus 35.1

Transportation Group works with Austin economic development organizations to assess the potential of job creation and value of technological innovation and resulting expertise.

Transportation Sector Need Number Six

Explore the potential of a public transportation and PTD system interface.

Probus 36.1

Transportation Group works with Capital Metro and DOT. RFP for prototype design is developed and submitted to DOT/DOE.

Transportation Sector Need Number Seven

Assess the potential of widespread telework programs and explore how to enhance the telework work place through the creation of virtual as well as actual workplace environments.

Probus 37.1

Transportation Group works with major employers to develop software and strategy for enhancing the virtual workplace. TG helps develop RFP with DOE, DOT, and SECO to develop software package with software developers. Develop and test prototype of neighborhood virtual workplace. (RFP)

Transportation Sector Need Number Eight

Assess the potential of widespread ride and car sharing.

Probus 38.1

Transportation Group develops ride-sharing plan and develops prototype plan with Capital Metro. Strategic partnership is developed for car sharing and prototype program is tested.

Transportation Sector Need Number Nine

Assess the public appeal of an elevated public transportation system.

Probus 39.1

Transportation Group works with Capital Metro and other civic groups to design and project costs for elevated mass transit with and without PTD integration. COF Transportation Group creates larger subgroup.

Transportation Sector Need Number Ten

Design and determine the costs of an extensive system of sidewalks and right of ways for human powered vehicles, small PTDs, and pedestrians.

Probus 40.1

With help from DOT and DOE, Transportation Group works with bicycle, pedestrian, and electric and light vehicle groups to link city through various strategies and scenarios. Working with Great Streets Coordinator, a starter line is envisioned and brought to the community for funding and construction.

BUILDINGS

Built Environment Need Number One

Assess the total amount of efficiency available in the residential and commercial sectors at varied levels of capital outlays using various efficiency programs.

Probus 41.1

Establish efficiency center with state of the art efficiency improvements for existing homes and commercial retail.

Built Environment Need Number Two

Determine how Austin Energy might further increase its revenue stream through an expansion into those markets.

Probus 42.1

Monitor efficiency and lighting center and determine how income stream can be maximized by leveraging of AE marketing assets. Monitor response from bill stuffers and other existing AE marketing efforts.

Built Environment Need Number Three

Determine and assess the potential of aggressive programs designed to provide combined heating, chilled water and off-peak storage for the commercial and industrial sectors.

Probus 43.1

Establish goals and marketing plan with existing chilled water and district heating and cooling programs. Establish link between planning department and AE.

Create more districts such as downtown loop. Work with major employers and school districts and universities in the planning stage of expansion of campuses.

Built Environment Need Number Four

Determine and assess the total potential of the built environment for solar access. (Including parking lots and garages)

Probus 44.1

COF Tech Committee works with existing solar program developers. Aerial photos and land development statistics are employed to estimate solar potential in the built environment. Particular emphasis is placed on the commercial sector with flat roofs and load profiles that are consistent with the resource.

Future Building Need Number One

Through the Green Building Program, determine and/or develop with strategic partner a cost effective reflective roofing with integrated PV generation.

Probus 45.1

Future Buildings Committee made up of COF Tech committee, AE Green Building, Planning, PV industry, and roofing industry, develops RFP for cost effective reflective roofing with PV integration to be submitted to SECO and DOE. Strategic alliances are established on a probationary basis and evaluated.

Future Building Need Number Two

Develop through Green Building a zero net energy or 120 house or structure design program to meet future growth in the residential and commercial sectors.

Probus 46.1

AE Green Building works with existing green building network of developers and builders to create a series of Zero Net Energy homes and structures which maximize efficiency, siting, solar gain, shade, bioshading, and other techniques in conjunction with PV, integrated PTD, and DG, to demonstrate various approaches and strategies to zero and 120 buildings. RFP developed for SECO/DOE.

Future Building Need Number Three

Promote and develop Smart House Technology.

Probus 47.1

Future Building Committee works with high tech industry and Clean Energy Incubator to develop computerized structure capable of controlling itself in future time by various methods and strategies. Reverse RFP is developed.

Future Building Need Number Four

Promote and develop Integrated Structural PV Power Glazings for Commercial High Rise Structures.

Probus 48.1

FBC and GB work with large architectural firms and AIA. RFP with DOE. AE Green Building develops program which encourages initial deployment through incentives or other creative programs.

Future Building Need Number Five

Determine the potential of co-powering structures through a symbiosis of PTDs and DG.

Probus 49.1

Initiate a study through a joint collaboration of COF Tech Committee, Future Buildings Committee, and Transportation Committee. Series of demonstration homes and structures are developed with several different vendors and /or strategic alliances. Total strategy is marketed and packaged as the Power Plant of the Future.

ACTUS

ACTUS will take the knowledge, experience, and resources gained in the PROBUS section of each MATRIX and deploy, if appropriate, the policy or technology on a significant scale.

THE ELECTRIC SECTOR

THE UTILITY OF THE FUTURE

The Sustainable Utility of the Future will look very different from the Utility of Today.

Unlike the present day utility, the Utility of the Future would be a balance of centralized and distributed technologies. To quote the EPRI Technology Roadmap, "Revolutionary advancements appear likely in the field of distributed generation over the next 10 years and beyond. As these technologies are developed, small-scale distributed generation and storage systems can become valuable new elements of the distributed utility of the future."

Rather than meeting load growth in large lumpy acquisitions of 500 MWs or more, the Utility of the Future will be able to grow its ability to meet the needs of its customers as its customer base grows.

The Utility of the Future will experience more and more decarbonization. Quoting EPRI's Roadmap, "Considerable energy decarbonization progress has occurred over the last two centuries, facilitated to an ever greater degree in this century by electricity. In the early part of the 19th century, wood yielded in time to coal, and in this century to oil and natural gas-each with progressively less carbon per unit of energy. Decarbonization has made further inroads with the introduction of nuclear and commercial renewable energy. This progress, if maintained through technology advancement, puts the world on a predictable trajectory toward a clean, electricity and hydrogen based energy economy.

"As the world economy electrifies, coal and oil can drop from more than 60% of the global energy mix today to the margin by 2100. In the past, decarbonization has occurred as a natural outcome of the economic drive for cost reduction and efficiency improvement. In the future, the economic drivers will be supplemented by environmental concerns, related Global Greenhouse Gas emissions, and other pollutants from fossil fuels."

THE SUSTAINABLE UTILITY

Depending on which strategy emerges from the Matrix and which technology proves superior in Probus, the right strategy of resources and technologies can be employed to assure that Austin Energy is a leader in environmental stewardship and the best community based electric utility that it can be.

Yet it is helpful, and instructive, to imagine what such a system might look like and how its constituents would work together to provide a reliable sustainable utility. The following represents one possible combination of resources and technologies that can be employed to sustainably meet the electrical needs of Austin in the next 25 years:

		Total	Res	Comm	Indust	
GWHS	2013	14,000	4,600	6,500	2,900	
	2028	20,000				
Peak Demand	2013	3,100 MW				
	2028	4,500 MW				

Fuel Mix	Coal	Gas	Nuclear	Renew
2000	46%	29%	25%	1%
2010 base	35%	35%	25%	5%
2013 scenario 1	35%	30%	25%	10%
2013 scenario 2	25%	25%	25%	25%
2028 scenario 1	22%	22%	25%	31%
2028 scenario 2	0%	20%	0%	80%

Major Sustainable Programs Implemented (Scenario 2)

	GWH 2013	GWH 2028
Bulk Wind	1,500	3,000
Storage	500	2,000
Hydrogen trans and storage		
Bulk Solar	500	3,000
Hydrogen trans and storage		
Residential Solar and DG		
DHW	100	300
PV and DG	100	2,000
Commercial Solar and DG		
CHW	100	200
PV and DG	300	2,000
Industrial Cogeneration and District C&H	100	1,000
Efficiency and GB	1,500	4,000
Hydrogen Conversions	0	8,000
Transportation Unitization	500	4,000
TOTAL (GWHS)	4,700	27,500

Descriptions of Programs:

Bulk Wind

Current wind program is expanded to 500 MW by 2013 and 1000 MW by 2028.

Bulk Solar

The program contemplates new Bulk Solar Power Plants of 250 MW by 2013 and 1500 MW by 2028.

Residential Solar Program

All homes that are sited favorably are fitted with PVs. DHW program replaces all electric hot water where homes have favorable sitting.

Commercial

All rooftops and parking facilities are inventoried and employed if site is appropriate.

Distributed Generation

Reversible fuel cell program or hydrogen microturbine deployed on a neighborhood level.

Efficiency and Green Building

New homes are expected to provide 120% of need. Old homes are brought up to highest achievable standards. Appliance program provided.

Hydrogen Conversion and Decommissioning

Fayette and Decker plants converted to Hydrogen combined cycle. STNP is entombed and converted to low heat turbine generation.

Transportation Unitization

Public and Private Electric Fleet developed, hybrid fleet integrated into grid.

The Electric Utility Industry is undergoing some of the greatest changes of its young 120-year history. The conservative approach of the past is yielding to the forces and pressures of the moment and the near future. Competition, advancements in technology, and environmental constraints are all going to force change.

Moving towards a decarbonized sustainable utility may ultimately prove to be the new conservative approach of the successful Electric Utility of The Future in this age of change.

As the EPRI road map states:

> "Sustainability tomorrow requires our urgent commitment today."

THE TRANSPORTATION SECTOR

THE UNIFIED TRANSPORTATION SYSTEM

"The inherently underutilized storage and power generation capacities of new hybrid electric vehicles could be connected to serve residential and commercial building loads", states the EPRI roadmap. "During the majority of time when vehicles are not being operated, they could provide an extensive distributed power generation and storage network. If for example, 1 million such vehicles were on the road in the year 2010, they could contribute 50-100GW of generating capacity, or about 5-10% of anticipated US capacity."

If these vehicles or Personal Transportation Devices were fueled by hydrogen or electrically powered by sustainable resources and yet capable of being part of an overall larger transportation strategy and infrastructure, our cities could see the end of the pollution and air degradation they currently must abide.

The ACTUS segment of this plan will not just be determined by the advent of fuel cell technologies or hydrogen fueled micro-turbine hybrids, but by the citizenry as well. New roads for pedestrians and lightweight electric PTDs will be developed only if the transportation architecture of our present day is reconsidered. This architecture of freeways and large retail destinations exists because of inexpensive energy and inexpensive land in the suburbs. Once these ingredients are no longer available, then new vibrant neighborhoods will emerge.

TELETRANSPORTATION

Telework could substantially change the amount of traffic on our rush hour freeways. It can certainly be used as an agent to reschedule the workday to reduce traffic congestion.

Telework neighborhood centers with childcare can make substantial changes in the way we work and our need to transport our bodies when it is often our ideas and creativity that need to be ransported. Much of our transportation may be replaced by advanced software that allows the virtual workplace to compete with the actual workplace.

BUILDINGS

ZERO ENERGY BUILDINGS

With the advancement of materials and knowledge, our buildings will become smarter and more independent. They will become entities to themselves much like large robots. They will know the weather that is coming. They will be able to respond to weather before it comes. They will provide their own energy. They may collect their own water. They will heat that water. They will recycle that water and their other waste streams.

They will have carpet inside that does not offgas harmful odors. That carpet may be leased from a carpet provider and recycled. They will have built in recycling bins for all kinds of waste and recycling.

Zero Energy Buildings will allow the Utility of the Future and the Community of the Future to grow naturally. They are the Future.

Chapter Seven

Never Leave *that till* Tomorrow, Which You *can do* Today

Recently, the Energy Foundation published a piece in California depicting and lamenting the fact that California had lost its leadership position in the development of renewable energy to Texas.

True, in 2001, more wind power was installed in Texas than any other state. If Texas was a nation, it would have been number three in the growth of renewable energy behind Germany and Spain. There are over 1100 MWs of wind turbines in the windfields in and around the mesas surrounding the Pecos River.

In a meeting not so long ago, some one asked me what, in my opinion, was the basis for the success of Texas Renewable Energy Policy and development. My cavalier response was "We like to be about nine years behind California."

This makes Ben Franklin's advice no less wise. But it does seem to add a corollary.

Never Leave That Till Tomorrow What You Can Do Today, unless you can do it better, smarter, and more efficiently tomorrow. When you are talking technology, that is just about all the time. Putting off decisions until tomorrow or the next day often pays dividends. A perfect example is in the Texas windfields. Instead of field after field of rather antiquated wind technology, the Texas windfields are beautiful, majestic installations of giant 1 MW turbines turning slowly and reliably on the horizon. Had we installed this much windpower just a few years ago, it would have been less reliable and certainly more cluttered and more expensive.

Technology is improving almost everything at a rather remarkable pace. Thomas Homer Dixon in his book "The Ingenuity Gap" discusses humankind's progress in providing light. Beginning with fires in caves perhaps a million years ago, we have made some serious progress. We started using stone lamps that burned fat maybe 30,000 years ago. Candlesticks were found in Crete and Egypt 5,000 years ago. There was a Babylonian market for lighting fuel a thousand years later. In 1272, Paris tax rolls listed 72 candle makers. Tallow candles were used throughout the Middle Ages. Not until the late 1700s was the Argand Oil Lamp used. London initiated gas street lighting in 1820. The electric discharge lamp was demonstrated in London as the American Civil War was gaining steam. Edison invented the carbon filament lamp in 1879. The Peal Street Station opened in 1882 with the first electric service. Then came high-pressure mercury discharge in the 20s, mercury vapor in the 30s, sodium vapor almost immediately thereafter, and the compact fluorescent in the 80s. Compact fluorescents get better, more affordable and more likable every time I go to Home Depot.

William Nordhaus , an economist at Yale, has studied the historic trend of the continued efficiency of lighting. He has concluded that the efficiency of light production has improved by a factor of 30,000 from the cave dweller fire to the compact fluorescent of today. Since the time of the Babylonian lamp, efficiency has improved 1200 fold. He also gauged the cost of providing light. He concludes that an hour's work today will provide 350 thousand times as much illumination as could be bought in early Babylonia.

"One modern one-hundred watt incandescent bulb burning for three hours each night would produce 1.5 million lumen hours of light per year. At the beginning of the 19th century, obtaining this amount of light would have required burning seventeen thousand candles, and the average worker would have had to toil almost one thousand hours to earn the dollars to buy the candles."

A new compact fluorescent is three times better than that.

The longer we wait to change out the bulbs in our homes with more efficient bulbs, the better the replacements will be and the more economical they will be in providing the light we need.

But then, there is this concept of opportunity costs. How much money would you have saved if you had replaced those light bulbs 7 years ago? You might have saved enough money to take that trip your wife always wanted. How much pollution would have been avoided? Would one child have one less asthma attack if you had polluted the air less for those seven years?

Sometimes, time runs out.

Sometimes, a point of no return is reached. The die is cast, so to speak.

Sometimes, adding the last pebble on a scale changes the weight on the scale and the scale moves quickly and completely. The balance is altered fundamentally.

> *The Moving Finger writes;*
> *and having writ, Moves on;*
> *nor all your Piety nor Wit*
> *Shall lure it back to cancel half a Line,*
> *Nor all your Tears wash out a Word of it.*
>
> *Omar Khayyam, 11th Century*

Maybe Ben Franklin knew that.

So the question is one of balancing the ever developing march of technology with the ever present needs of the moment. Do I need a new computer now or can I wait until a faster computer comes along? Can I make my car work for another year? Will the house not deteriorate too much if I defer painting it for one more year? Can I afford to not fix the roof now that it is leaking and the incoming water damage is beginning to take its toll on the structure itself, as well as the inhabitants inside?

Can we afford to continue to pollute our own house, our air, and rob our children of the most economical fuels without changing a fundamental balance or permanently damaging the very structure of the house itself?

At what point do we act because we know that to not act is a recipe for destruction.

Indeed at this moment, the discourse of the World is centered on that question. The need for security and for energy presents the awful and destructive course of War before us.

Would we not further our own purpose and our own security by wholly and substantially committing to the development of sustainable technologies that protect us now and into the future?

THE COMMITMENT OF THE FUTURE

In 1981, there were 213 host computers on the Internet. In seven years, there were 100,000. Four years after that there were a million. Two years later there were two million. Two years after that, 10 million. As we moved into the millennium, there were 100 million. Today, the number is somewhere around 200 million.

There were not a million cell phone subscribers until 1985. Ten years later there were 100 million. There are over a billion today-roughly the amount of landlines in existence. Over 80 % of the inhabitants of Luxemburg have a mobile phone. There is a slightly smaller percentage for the residents of Hong Kong. Over 70% of the inhabitants (including children) of Taiwan, Austria, Norway, Italy, the United Kingdom, Finland, Sweden and Israel have a cell phone. The United States has a 40% saturation. China has a 7 % saturation, but it is the second largest market after the US. In Africa the number of cell phones surpassed the number of landlines in 2001. Most are prepaid.

The production of solar cells grew from 0.1 megawatts in 1971 to 7 megawatts in 1980. In 1990, annual production was 40 megawatts. 2002 will see almost 400 megawatts produced.

Wind energy has grown from a total of 10 megawatts in 1980, to 1000 MW in 1985. By 1998 there were 10,000 megawatts installed. There will be almost 30,000 megawatts by the end of 2002.

In 1988 there were 45 million fluorescent lamps sold worldwide. That number doubled in three years. There were almost a half billion sold in 2000, 100 million of them in North America.

The growth of solar, wind, and efficiency is truly impressive, but not when it is compared to the computer and cell phone industries. If the sales of PV had grown like the growth of computers connected to the Internet, there would be an astounding million and a half MWs of PV manufactured every year. That would supply one half of all the electricity used in the world in one year. Had PV grown like cell phones, it would be a thousand fold over its 1981 rate of 10 megawatts, or 10,000 MW every year. That would replace the generation in the United States in 7 years. At a continued growth rate, it would replace all generation in a matter of a few dozen months.

Things can and do change. And they can change dramatically.

At the end of 1944, a band of scientists were working overtime. They were developing a technology that would have profound effect on the war. There was no time to waste. The forces of destruction were at the door. The Manhattan Project helped end the war with Japan. But its genesis began before the war began.

Leo Szilard, like many other foreign-born physicists in the U.S. who had fled fascism, knew Germany was conducting nuclear research. Having learned the Germans had banned the export of uranium, he believed the Germans were developing an atomic bomb. Fearing what would happen if Germany developed a nuclear weapon, he urged Dr. Albert Einstein to convince the American government to support nuclear research.

On August 2, 1939, a month before Germany invaded Poland, Einstein wrote a letter to President Roosevelt recommending that the U.S. fund nuclear research, stating that it could result in "extremely powerful bombs" made of uranium. Einstein's recommendation was based on the research of Szilard and Enrico

Fermi. Szilard had developed the theory of nuclear fission. But it was Fermi who was the first to actually produce nuclear fission in the laboratory, which won him the 1938 Nobel Prize for Physics.

Based on Einstein's letter, President Roosevelt authorized a study, but the decision to devote full energy to the production of the bomb was not made until December 6, 1941-the day before the Japanese attack on Pearl Harbor.

General Leslie Groves was chosen to make the atomic bomb a reality, code-named the Manhattan Project. He named J. Robert Oppenheimer, a brilliant nuclear physicist from the University of California at Berkeley as director. Together they chose Los Alamos, New Mexico, a remote location not far from Santa Fe, as the site for the design and construction of atomic bombs. Oppenheimer gathered scientists, many of them Nobel Prize winners, from the most prestigious universities in the U.S.: University of California at Berkeley, University of Chicago, Columbia University, as well as several British and Canadian scientists.

The U.S. Army Corps of Engineers built power stations, factories, foundries, blast furnaces, steel works, hospitals, laboratories and housing at Los Alamos. It involved over 200,000 people and cost the U.S. two billion dollars. The Manhattan Project was a collaboration of American science and industry carried out under the direction of the U.S. Army. The Manhattan Project was conducted in complete secrecy not only from the enemy but also from the American public. Most of the factory workers were unaware of what they were producing.

The first atomic bomb tested at Trinity on July 16, 1945 proved that the U.S. was in possession of the most destructive weapon ever devised by man. The bomb was powered by the splitting of all the nuclei in several kilograms of plutonium. A sphere of plutonium, the size of a baseball, produced an explosion equal to 15,000 to 20,000 tons of TNT. When the bomb exploded at Trinity at 5:30 a.m., it vaporized the tower and turned asphalt around the base of the tower to green sand. Suddenly, the sky was brighter than several suns. Seconds after the explosion came a huge blast that sent withering heat across the desert.

A massive orange and yellow cloud in the shape of a mushroom surged and billowed upward reaching into the sub-stratosphere up to an elevation of 41,000 feet. A soldier 10,000 feet away was knocked off his feet by the force of the shock wave. The flash of light was seen more than ten miles away, and a soldier five miles away was temporarily blinded. The explosion was heard 50 miles away.

On the day of the test, Oppenheimer fully realized the enormity of what he had just accomplished. As he stood watching the mushroom cloud, he recalled later, a phrase from the Baghavad Gita, the Hindu scripture, floated through his mind, "I am become death, the destroyer of worlds."

When this country made a commitment to build the most destructive weapon ever devised by man, it did so. When this country made the commitment to go to the moon, it did so. Thomas Friedman, of the New York Times, has called for this country to make a commitment to the development of renewable energy similar to the commitment that we made in the War. He suggests that we begin a Manhattan style project to develop another energy system that is independent of the present energy system and its dependence on foreign oil and foreign natural gas.

We do have the National Lab for Renewable Energy in Colorado and there are other Labs throughout the country that are developing and testing various aspects of renewable energy. But the labs are not funded as if the well being of our country depends upon their success. There are not thousands and thousands of scientists working on the problems of bringing the cost of photovoltaic cells down to affordable levels. During the Manhattan Project, there were perhaps a quarter of a million people working on a project that they not only did not understand; they did not even know its purpose. Hundreds of millions of dollars were invested.

The result was the end of the war, the saving of many American lives, and the creation of a new science and a new industry.

A Manhattan Project to develop Solar and the solar hydrogen economy will require an equal effort. To reduce the cost of solar energy, so that our homes can be powered by photons that are converted to electrons, we must have a national and even global commitment that recognizes that the time to act is now, that we should not wait to do tomorrow what we can do today because we are running out of time. We are creating problems for ourselves and our progeny that will remain long after we have lived our short lives. If we choose not to act, we are choosing.

Such a Manhattan Project must be initiated by our leaders who comprehend fully the road that lies ahead. They must see and believe that it is incumbent upon them to forge a path of vision that provides an alternative to the present. We can have vibrant cities with intensive energy consumption without polluting the air we breathe. We can have a vibrant economy without changing the climate. We can power our homes and PTDs without depleting the natural resources with which we have been endowed. We can enjoy our lives now without prejudicing the lives of our children and their children.

The basic myth that you must balance economic development with environmental degradation is just that. It is true, that in a carbon burning economy, that the more economic development you desire, the more environmental degradation you must endure. This is not true of a solar hydrogen economy. A Solar Hydrogen Economy would change many of our basic myths about economic development. We would see that the once honored debate between development and degradation is a false debate. It is a debate based on the limitations imposed by the burning of carbon to provide our energy. It is a debate whose genesis began perhaps a million years ago when humankind first began to make fire.

We do not face an energy crisis.

We face a crisis of consciousness.

The Universe is not about to run out of energy. There is energy everywhere. In fact, as Einstein predicted and Oppenheimer proved, mass itself is energy. We are at the end of a very long road. Starting with gathered wood, then moving to peat and coal, to whale oil and plant oils, to rock oil and its sister natural gas, we have steadily developed in the art of using energy. Humankind's great adventure of converting from the present carbon, fire burning age we now know, to an age where the radiant energy that exists all around is transformed to usable energy is upon us now. We have only to recognize our condition and act responsibly.

We must act responsibly on the personal level, at the family level, the community level, the regional level, the national level, and the global level. A change of this historic magnitude will require leadership at each of these levels.

The vision that humankind is on the verge of a great future that has transcended the burning of carbon fuels is rather invigorating. The notion that the way we do things now is just not good enough has real power and potential. It opens us up to the possibility that life, as we know it, can be very different from the way it is now, and that a change of this magnitude can be very, very good for us, and perhaps even better for those who follow us.

In the next few decades, humankind will no longer need to burn carbon. We will more likely use the carbon we have placed in the air to build with that carbon through nanotechnology. We will no longer take resources out of the ground and smelt them like we did at the beginning of the Iron Age. We will no longer burn coal to make steam to drive a steam engine like we did at the beginning of the Industrial Age. We will no longer adhere to a belief that we must suffer a little bit of pollution if we are to prosper. We will understand with our computers and with our interface with these and other tools of the mind and of control that many of the beliefs that were held to be true during the height of the age of carbon were true only during the Age of Carbon.

As computers and humans become more and more integrated, we will truly see new horizons in the biosciences, in medicine, in physics, in our understanding of the universe, and our place in it. We will know and understand that the universe is full of energy. And we will know and understand the abundance we have been given.

THE COMMUNITY OF THE FUTURE

History provides us with a fairly short list of examples where certain communities somehow became beacons of the future or at least best practitioners of the present. Most great empires had a city or community where the big ideas originated. In the west, there was Greece and Athens. Then, there was Rome and its Empire. There was Madrid and Spain, Lisbon and Portugal, Napoleon and Paris, London and the British Empire, and today, New York and the hegemony of the United States.

It may seem a little presumptuous, if not a little silly to place Austin in this list of great communities. Yet, we know there is no way to be great except by trying to be great. Austin is uniquely situated in the State, in the Country, and in the World to emerge as a great Community.

When I first moved to Austin to come to the University of Texas, it was a fairly sleepy place. There was The University that let out during the summer. There was the State Legislature that met for 5 months every 2 years. There were a few high tech companies like Texas Instruments and I B M. Most of the rich people lived in West Austin between Lamar and the Lake. But there were not any really rich people. They were in Houston or Dallas, and in LA, and in Chicago, and in New York. Austin was a nice, sleepy little Capital with a growing music scene thanks to the Armadillo World Headquarters and a handful of other venues.

Then, something happened.

Austin City Limits became the most popular program on Public Television. With the help of 4th of July Picnics, and the constant inflow of musicians and songwriters, Austin slowly but surely became the Live Music Capital of the World. Hardly any one who knows or cares about music has not heard of Austin, Texas.

As the music scene grew, so did a completely different scene. With the help of a UT student who started selling computers from his dorm room, Austin began to be known as a high tech town. Today, the number of computers coming from Austin can stand up against even the largest of the world's cities. With the nineties and the Internet came more companies and more software writers. Hardly anyone who knows or cares about high tech and computers has not heard of Austin, Texas.

Last year, the Clean Energy Incubator began to look for companies to help develop. This offshoot of The University of Texas and the IC 2 Institute is looking to make Austin the Capital of Clean Energy.

There is a growing critical mass here in Austin than can create a clean energy scene that marries the style of a community that loves music and art, with a community that embraces the realities and potential of the technologies of the future.

What we need is not the Manhattan Project but the Austin Energy Project.

Here in Austin, we can forge a nexus of University assets with the assets found in our semiconductor and software companies with the assets of a well-educated Citizenry. We have an electric utility that has the best green building program, the best efficiency programs, and the best green pricing program for clean energy in the country.

When you include the City of San Antonio, and the Lower Colorado River Authority, the resulting public power authority is the largest in the United States.

We have the potential to lead the World in providing the new technologies that the World will need. Hardly anyone who knows or cares about the Future will not know about Austin, Texas.

For it is The Community of the Future.

FUTURELOGUE

When I woke up this morning, I looked up at the ceiling and smiled as I took in the soft glow of the new carbon-based surface that had been applied just two days before. It takes 24 hours for it to really start working. The light from the ceiling is actually pretty nice. I have been putting off installing the new lighting system because I was so fond of the old one. My house, by all standards, is a real antique now. Built in 1926, it is now 99 years old.

This new light source is, I must say, quite appealing. One, it hardly uses any electricity at all. Based on the same process and science of the now ubiquitous carbon based nano-materials that convert sunlight to electricity, these materials, acting in reverse, convert electricity back to photons. The glow is controllable and, of course, part of my overall smart house programming. It can be programmed to produce various colors and moods, but that is a little too much for me, so I am using the default morning light program.

I went downstairs and got the milk out of the refrigerator and poured it over the cereal that I buy from the HEB Whole Foods Store. I used to use a little cream, but no more. My 30-year old refrigerator was recently replaced with one of the new super-insulated, super-intelligent versions that actually makes the hot water for the house too. The newest fridges will even notify if you need to buy milk, and it will even order it for you. But I am way too old to get used to that. I still want to go down to the Coop and look. Old Fashion? No question.

The kitchen, like my bedroom, has one of these new whole room environment lights too.

It provides even, shadow free light throughout the room and it is easily and readily programmable. I use the daylight setting almost all the time. When I bake, I use the heat pump oven. It heats the food by cooling the room. My stove top runs on the hydrogen that is created in the reversible fuel cell that sits outside next to the air-conditioner.

In the evening, the kitchen ceiling light defaults back to a pleasant, almost candle like dining light as long as there is someone in the room. All of the lights throughout the house turn off when there is no one in the room. The room sensors can somehow sense your presence even if you are reading. If you are sleeping or you drop off to sleep while sitting in your ergo-chair, it seems to be able to know. Maybe it hears me breathing.

I still enjoy my old fake fireplace. Except for the fact that it now runs on hydrogen instead of natural gas, it is pretty much the same design I had 30 years ago.

I did add a sound system a few years back. It's embarrassing how much pleasure it gives me and my guests. In all fairness, it is a pretty impressive aural-visual illusion.

My house has one of those new super smart thermostats that not only knows the inside temperature, but the outside temperature as well. It controls the temperature and humidity level inside the house. It knows which direction the outside temperature is moving. It can prepare the house for future weather events because it receives data from the weather service. The new houses have all kinds of windows and venting opportunities that can be automatically deployed by the smart house computer. There are all kinds of security options that plug into the house computer too. I just can't seem to get the hang of it. I'm always setting something off. So I have just turned that feature off.

The air-conditioning unit outside takes the oftentimes oppressively hot air, then uses it as the energy source to create the cool air that comes inside. It needs a little outside electricity to start the cycle, but once it starts running, it draws less energy than an old style light bulb. That's a good thing, too, because the air-conditioning unit runs almost all the time with the warming we've experienced. Necessity really is the mother of invention. Since climate change really took off 15 years ago, the idea of heating your house has pretty much disappeared into memory and into the weather record books. Our climate here in Central Texas is now more like the old climate of Corpus Christi, without the wind or the salt.

The collapse of the brief, but not undramatic era of competitive electricity at the turn of the century created a unique opportunity for Public Power. I actually do go to the office a couple of times a week. The rest of the time, I telework using the Company's Virtual Office Software. (CVOS) With all of the cameras, views, and different perspectives provided, I can pretty much feel connected no matter where I am.

My wireless connection works almost everywhere in the city now. Each year when I get my new Computator, I marvel how they continue to get smaller and smaller. The new ones can project holographicly into thin air. Mine still projects onto a screen wall. Most surfaces are now wall screen capable. The language interphaser is finally relatively flawless. Five years ago, they were reasonably reliable, but sometimes comically unpredictable and occasionally embarrassing. My Computator is powered by my power shirt. It not only helps keep me cool, the imbedded nanofibers turns that body heat into enough current to run my PC and my other personal appliances.

When I do go to the office, I take the tubes if I am in a hurry. The new Crystal Line actually runs above the City with continuous views of the Hill Country and Skyline.

I can go from the 23rd Street Station to the Palmer Auditorium Node in about 6 minutes.

At work, I use a Segway HT5 to zip around town. It's been a long time since I have even been in a car. (Even though I would welcome the chance to try out my new eyes with their night vision implants.) When I have time, and I often do, I walk on the elevated skyways that criss-cross the city. They are sheltered from the rain with a clear carbon based photovoltaic covering that allows the light to come through a little bluer. That makes the sky viewed from below a royal almost indigo blue. With all of the HTs, (human transporters), joggers, cyclists, and walkers, it is rare when I don't run into an old friend to visit.

I have seen reports that, at any given time from early morning to very late in the evening, these skywalks are more or less constantly utilized by an average of 100,000 adults and 50,000 minors. That is almost 5% of the population!

Just 22 years ago, we made a commitment at The Utility to lead the Nation and the State in the development of sustainable energy. At the time it seemed risky-even to me.

It was the Citizenry that made it happen. The huge vote of support to move away from a carbon based energy system to a solar hydrogen system gave the marching orders we needed to move in bold and creative ways.

Who would have imagined that from such humble beginnings just 135 years ago, that a relatively small city electric utility from a small capital in the southern United States would grow to become one of the great public providers of energy, transportation, and communication services? With gross revenues of $100 billion a year and profits of over 2 billion, our profits have eliminated the need for property and sales tax in the greater Austin metropolitan area.

Our public transportation systems are the envy of the World and our per capita income is now in the top five. Even with a waiting time now of 30 to 40 months, requests to take up residence here in Austin have reached an all time high.

I found an old bumper sticker while going through my flat files looking at some old Armadillo World Headquarters posters last night.

It said, "Keep Austin Weird"

Weird.

RECOMMENDATIONS

In a complex and interrelated plan, it is difficult and sometimes unwise to try to distill such complexity into simple elements. Yet, ironically, such focus is generally necessary to hone any plan of action to its most essential elements. The following recommendations are offered with that understanding:

Recommendation One

Austin Energy should continue the Community of the Future Initiative and fully embrace the Austin Energy Project and the plan herein to create a sustainable solar hydrogen economy.

Recommendation Two

City Council should pass a Resolution authorizing Austin Energy and other relevant City Departments to move aggressively to investigate, develop and initiate the transition to a sustainable solar hydrogen economy.

Recommendation Three

Austin Energy should procure renewable energy at prices below the green rate and offer the green rate as an alternative fixed rate to all new customers.

Recommendation Four

Austin Energy should redefine itself in order to maximize its potential and service to the Community.

Recommendation Five

The City of Austin should seek alliances with other Public Power entities to increase market power and reduce risks.

Recommendation Six

A new Central Texas Alliance of governmental units, education institutions, non-profit organizations, and the private sector should adopt a new vision of Energy, Sustainability, and Service.

Recommendation Seven

The City of Austin should actively petition the State of Texas to aggressively promote the development of the solar-hydrogen economy.

ABOUT THE AUTHOR

Michael J. Osborne is an author, inventor, policy maker, and futurist. He has served on the Steering Committees of the State of Texas Energy Policy Partnership and the Sustainable Energy Development Task Force under Governor Ann Richards and was appointed to the Texas Energy Coordinating Council by Governor George Bush. In 1998, The Austin City Council appointed Mr. Osborne to the Resource Management Commission where he served as its Chairman.

His first book, Lightland, about the transition from a carbon-based economy to a solar hydrogen-based economy is available in Bookstores and at Amazon.com.